'A brave, frank and illuminating [...] wrought so much pain in fam[...] Jesse Fink, *Inside Sport*

'This courageous book will help su[...] and their families.' *Good Reading*

'There are so many people suffering from mental illness and it is so uplifting to see that it can be beaten. Craig's is a fascinating story, one that will endear itself to everyone in our community.' Paul Harragon, Newcastle Knights premiership-winning captain

'A startling and gripping story.' Lucy Clark, *Sunday Telegraph*

'ABC sports reporter Craig Hamilton wins the award for bravest biography of the year.' *Daily Telegraph*

'*Broken Open* skilfully carries you through Hamilton's illness and his recovery. The insight is so remarkable it takes you on a journey that is almost too tangible.' *West Australian*

'A must-read story of remarkable triumph that will inspire anyone who reads it.' Wayne Bennett, Brisbane Broncos coach and bestselling author of *Don't Die with the Music in You*

'Craig's story speaks to everyone and helps to reduce the stigma associated with mental illness. With humour, honesty and touching vulnerability he highlights how acceptance of illness is an important first step to recovery.' *SANE Australia*, which named *Broken Open* as 2005 Book of the Year

'This is an important book. It is blunt, uncomplicated and direct ... Most importantly, it offers hope. It describes the personal and professional partnerships that need to be in place to promote recovery and resumption of a productive life.' Professor Ian Hickie, clinical advisor, *beyondblue: the national depression initiative*

BROKEN OPEN

CRAIG HAMILTON
with NEIL JAMESON

BANTAM
SYDNEY • AUCKLAND • TORONTO • NEW YORK • LONDON

BROKEN OPEN
A BANTAM BOOK

First published in Australia and New Zealand in 2004 by Bantam
This edition first published in 2005 by Bantam

National Library of Australia
Cataloguing-in-Publication Entry

Hamilton, Craig.
Broken open.

ISBN 978 1 86325 515 8.
ISBN 1 86325 515 X.

1. Hamilton, Craig. 2. Sportscasters – Australia –
Biography. 3. Mentally ill – Australia – Biography. 4.
Mentally ill – Family relationships. I. Jameson, Neil,
1953–. II. Title.

070.449796092

Transworld Publishers,
a division of Random House Australia Pty Ltd
20 Alfred Street, Milsons Point, NSW 2061
http://www.randomhouse.com.au

Random House New Zealand Limited
18 Poland Road, Glenfield, Auckland

Transworld Publishers,
a division of The Random House Group Ltd
61-63 Uxbridge Road, Ealing, London W5 5SA

Random House Inc
1745 Broadway, New York, New York 10036

Cover photograph: Getty Images
Author photograph: Simone Thurtell
Cover design by Darian Causby/Highway 51 Design Works
Typeset by Midland Typesetters, Maryborough, Victoria
Printed and bound by Griffin Press, South Australia

10 9 8 7 6 5 4 3

For Louise, Joshua, Amy and Laura.

CONTENTS

FOREWORD

Craig Hamilton has one key message in writing his story. It is for Australian men and it is important: Don't let your pride or stubbornness prevent you reaching out for help when you need it.

I know Craig went through his own anguish with mental illness and if it can affect him it can affect anybody. I hold him in high esteem as I believe him to be very credible and someone who has a real passion for what he does, particularly calling rugby league on the ABC.

Like many Australians today, Craig changed his life so he could manage his illness. Through medication and a healthy lifestyle of yoga, meditation and laughter he is now living a healthy life. His story is a must-read. His triumph is truly remarkable and will inspire anyone lucky enough to read it.

Sadly many people suffering mental illness do not have the strength or support to change their lives. Like Craig I have watched players and have friends and family who have suffered from mental illness. I know through these experiences that mental illness exists and is not in someone's imagination as we are often told.

By telling his story I know Craig will help others who have suffered, but more importantly he makes us all much more aware of the presence of mental illness, and in particular depression and bipolar disorder.

Sincerely

Wayne Bennett
Director Coaching
Brisbane Broncos

PROLOGUE

TUESDAY, 12 SEPTEMBER 2000

Today I felt pass over me a breath of wind from
the wings of madness.
Charles Baudelaire

It's a five-minute drive from our home in suburban New-castle to Broadmeadow railway station. In the budding brightness of this spring day my wife, Louise, is at the wheel and I am next to her in the passenger seat. The kids – Joshua, nine; Amy, seven; and Laura, three – are in the back, excited about delivering their dad into the global tide of professionals and bit players converging on the harbour city to power up the biggest show on the planet – the Sydney Olympic Games.

Hello world. This is Australia calling. From the lanyard around my neck hangs a media accreditation tag – my permit for passage anywhere and everywhere at the Olympics. Beneath the passport-size snap are printed the

1

words: 'Craig Hamilton, Broadcaster, ABC Radio'. Whatever my professional career delivers – past and future – this is as good as it gets. Three days until the opening ceremony. My bag is packed and on this flawless afternoon we're walking together as a family from car park to ticket gate and . . .

. . . and something is not quite right.

Unsighted, a major piece of space junk that has been orbiting our lives for a long time is about to crash out of a clear blue sky and transform this perfect scene. At the core of my being, a chain of detonations is firing up, gathering intensity on its way to the big bang. But, right now, it takes the shape of hyper stimulation, a symptom that might be explained away by the wonder and excitement of this long-anticipated day. In reality, and undiagnosed at this point, I'm in the manic phase of bipolar disorder, riding the face of a tsunami-size mania and set to wipe out in awesome and truly awful style.

Forty-eight hours earlier my mood had become elevated to the point where I had lost my grip on reality. At the time, I didn't know. They tell me you never do.

Now, if this tale is not weird enough already, then try this: *in my mind I had become Jesus Christ reincarnate.*

This is delusion on the grandest scale. The Jesus notion hadn't struck me like a lightning bolt but, rather, taken shape as a result of the escalating mania throwing off grandiose delusions. And they don't come any more grandiose. All the events of my life to that point had been readying me for this occasion, or so I thought. In the two days before arriving at the railway station my Olympics planning had changed. I had a new assignment. It was perfectly clear: I was going to change the world. My gospel for the global audience was disarm, feed the hungry and love one another.

A wise man once said that insanity is a perfectly rational adjustment to an insane world. My message was rational, noble and universal. The only flaw was that the messenger was, by any definition, insane.

The plan was that I would arrive at the Games as Christ. With the exception of a few enlightened souls, nobody would know that the Messiah had returned. I would do my broadcast job for the ABC and, during the course of the fifteen days of the Olympics, it would become apparent to the movers and shakers gathered in Sydney that Christ was among them and they would afford Him the opportunity to speak at the closing ceremony. To add lustre and credibility to the occasion, I would be sharing the stage with Nelson Mandela. The message would be heard by the planet.

———

On the station we bump into Kathy Stewart, wife of my long-time mate Chris Williams. Kathy runs the rail kiosk, is pleased to see us and, as we exchange hugs, she tells us that Chris will be dropping by shortly. Kathy and Chris have been very close to us. I was emcee at their wedding and they were honoured guests at our ceremony. Chris and I had been cricketing club mates for ten years and had opened the bowling together. It will be great to see him, I say.

The pressure in the volcano is rising.

Don't misjudge this. I am not feeling bad. On the contrary, I am feeling ten foot tall, bulletproof and experiencing a high I'd imagine you could attain only on the strongest drugs.

I want to see Chris so I let the first train come and go without me. I'm in control here, or so I believe. Louise thinks otherwise. Unease chafes at her caring heart. Call it women's intuition or put it down to her twenty years as a nurse, she senses a rupture in the fault line, but she can't put her finger on it. Family duty calls and she and the kids have to go.

On the point of their departure I sit down on a bench and start giggling to myself. The kids ask me what I'm laughing at and I tell them it doesn't matter. I can't tell my kids that I have been seized by the realisation that life is a big joke and the sooner everybody wakes up to that fact the better humankind will be. Everything, especially ourselves, is taken too seriously. This insight has set me giggling. *I am in on The Big Joke.*

I miss the darts of disquiet in my wife's concerned eyes as she stoops to kiss me, gathers up the kids and departs.

Alone on the bench, I continue to reflect on the absurdity of The Big Joke, laughing out loud. It must be apparent to the half-dozen or so travellers waiting for the next train that my shackles are broken. I place my head in my hands and my mood starts morphing from hilarity into a cosmic scramble of visions from history. The noise of a passing train, the sound of footsteps – any external influence becomes the stimulus for another jumping vision as my internal teleplay flashes through the ages and pages of history. It is like watching a movie, my mind is way behind the plot, but I don't want it to end. I need to see what comes next.

'Are you okay?' It is Kathy's voice and her warm arm across my shoulders.

No response.

'Look, Chris is here. He's come to see you.'

'Hamo!' I recognise Chris's voice.

Again, no response as I keep my eyes covered with my hands.

'Hamo, how ya going, mate?'

Without a word, I stand and walk away down the length of the platform. Chris, bewildered, follows. 'Hamo, what's going on?'

I turn to eyeball him. 'Fuck off!' I say.

'Hamo, it's me.'

'Fuck off!'

On any other day and with any other bloke, I would cop a smack in the mouth. But Chris Williams is a caring, compassionate individual. He knows now that the gears are stripped. My welfare is his priority.

He tries to reason with me. I respond with louder, more violent abuse. 'Listen,' I say in exasperation, 'you're dead, I'm dead, we're all dead, *everybody* is dead. I'm now in some other space, so just fuck off!'

'What are you talking about, Hamo?' he says evenly. 'We're fine, I'm fine, you're fine, you're going to the Olympics –'

'Stop talking shit and *just fuck off.*'

Kathy witnesses the entire exchange and phones Louise with the advice that she better return, pronto.

My wife parks the car again and ushers the kids into Kathy's care inside the kiosk. She is fearful of what they might witness on the platform. Louise screws up her nerve and, under the wretched gaze of strangers, steps out into that corridor to confront God-knows-what.

She sees two men. One is her husband and the father of her children and he is ranting at the top of his voice, yelling illogical, foul-mouthed abuse at one of his dearest friends who is doing his level best to placate him.

I am hostile, enraged, out of control.

Years in general nursing and especially in drug and alcohol rehabilitation have given Louise some experience of psychosis. She recognises the symptoms.

'He's psychotic,' she says, 'call Mental Health.'

———

The Mental Health Crisis Team wants to know the details. They are: we have a man in his late thirties, storming up and down the platform, yelling and screaming abuse, out of control, he is psychotic.

The combination of 'railway station' and 'out of control' are enough. Mental Health advises that the police must be called. At this point, let's get one thing clear: I had no intention of jumping under a train or doing anybody harm. But no-one else knew that.

The police paddy wagon backs up into the loading ramp. I am still stalking the platform like a wild thing, yelling and abusing anyone who comes near. As the police approach, Chris steps aside. The officers – maybe six of them – string themselves along the platform edge to prevent the possibility of me jumping in front of a train. This loose line of blue then loops in behind me, gently herding me in the direction of the paddy wagon.

When I see two officers standing either side of the open door it occurs to me they are going to put me in their van.

'I'm not going in there.' All indignation and confusion. 'I'm not a criminal . . . I'm going to the Olympics.'

The phalanx of blue moves closer. Instantly, the survival instinct kicks in. Fight or flight. Frantically, I examine the options. Access back to the platform is blocked by an arc of blue uniforms. There is nowhere to run. *I must fight.*

I am a wild, thrashing, kicking, bucking animal scrapping for its very life. I flail, twist, heave and roll on the ground, scuffing shoes, ruining attire. I weigh no more than 85 kilograms, but it takes the combined effort of all the officers to restrain me, pin my arms behind my back, snap the handcuffs into place and heave me into the wagon.

Abruptly, I realise I am free of their grip. But there is no time to react. The metal door swings shut. With dreadful finality, the bolt slams into place.

1

RADIO DAZE

From the outside, my life had looked so normal: family, mortgage, job. An ordinary house in a regular suburban street; an ordinary car snug in the garage; dog romping in the yard. To so many intents and so many purposes, this was our existence. This was the Hamiltons: Craig, Louise, Joshua, Amy and Laura.

As a career option, broadcasting had been a late choice. I had worked eight years as a below-ground coalminer when a sunny Canberra afternoon in 1989 found me at one of life's intersections. Manuka Oval had been a rewarding field two years earlier when I had taken five wickets as the Newcastle representative side defeated the Australian Capital Territory. This time, the returns weren't as healthy as we struggled in the run chase on the way to defeat in the Country Cup final. The attention of the Newcastle blokes waiting in the pavilion was momentarily diverted by the approach of a stranger. He was from a local radio station broadcasting the game and needed a volunteer to add a few insights to the call. Recollecting my inclination to mimic cricket commentators, the boys volunteered me. If I had stayed where I was, declined the chance, I'd still be working down a mine today.

Twenty on-air minutes passed in a blink. It was a buzz, seemed to come easy and I would have done more if given the chance. A couple of cricket officials had been listening and, on returning to Newcastle, they and the side's captain, Greg Arms, hatched a plan to let me loose on an unsuspecting public as an honorary publicity officer. The brief was simple: be a spokesperson for the game. From there, it began to snowball. I became the voice of cricket on local radio. If the television station needed a comment, I was the guy they interviewed. From phone reports I eventually made it into the studio to sit behind a microphone. A foot, or a toe at least, was in the door.

I was delivering regular news reports for local commercial stations when Brian Burke, a former representative rugby league player then working for ABC Radio in Newcastle, invited me to file weekly previews for his Saturday morning sports show *All in the Game*. A few months later he decided to expand his show into a forum to chew over sporting issues of the day. By this stage I had fallen in love with the medium and when Brian called to offer me a chair on the panel, I was thrilled. Every Saturday morning I'd drive to the studio, do the *All in the Game* slot and then head off to play cricket. As that summer rolled on I became aware of a subtle shift in the attitude of both my team-mates and the opposition. I sensed some were thinking: 'Here's a bloke who could publicise what happens here today so I'd better make sure I'm not a headline for all the wrong reasons.'

My thinking at the time was just how easy this broad-casting business seemed, how natural it came to me and what a worthwhile contribution I was making to the one-hour Saturday morning show. I've listened to those tapes in recent times and nothing could be further from the truth. Hours would go by and I wouldn't even make a single comment. But, at the time, I thought I was pretty good.

Brian Burke left to join a local commercial broadcaster. The ABC station boss called an emergency meeting and proposed that I and another part-timer, Lindy Burns, host the show. Lindy had been a topline basketballer and was destined for a venerated career in broadcasting. Back then, we were both part-timers making our way, had much in common and worked well together. We would become a successful double act. Sure, we said.

'And another thing,' said the station boss, 'I suppose we'd better pay you!'

To that point my contribution had been purely volun-tary. Now, my wage for preparing and presenting my share of an hour of Saturday morning radio would be $80.

In 1992 the ABC's then Head of Sport for New South

Wales, Peter Longman, was looking for an around-the-grounds rugby league reporter to take care of the Newcastle Knights home games. My name was mentioned. Peter rang and offered me the position. Suddenly, I not only had to learn how to hook up the technology for a live feed from the ground, but had to discover the art of the quick, concise update and the technique of the interview.

My first dialogue was with Sydney Roosters coach Mark Murray, whose side had just played a 10-all draw with the Knights in the first game of the new season. My opening gambit went: 'You must be confident of making the semi-finals now.'

Peter Longman rang during the week. 'There's an art to the interview,' he said. 'It's round one, there's a lot of water to go under the bridge between now and the semis. Keep your powder dry and let the coach tell the story.' It was good advice.

Jim Maxwell had been doing an exceptional job as side-line eye for Peter Wilkins' match-of-the-day broadcast until called away for Commonwealth Games duty. An opportunity presented. Wilko enjoys a punt and he gambled on the novice from Newcastle. I filled the gig for three or four weeks and passed muster. During the following off-season it became apparent Jim would be away for long spells on overseas cricket tours. The job was mine. From 1995 I would be the ABC Radio's rugby league side-line eye for its broadcasts throughout New South Wales and Queensland.

It was a crowded life. On Saturday and Sunday I worked

for the ABC in cities as removed as Melbourne and Brisbane. Monday to Friday I worked down the mine. My dream was to one day work in the media full-time. Our firstborn, Josh, had arrived in 1991, Amy in 1993 and Laura was due in 1997. A seven-day working week leaves little time to be Dad.

If there was a point to this frenetic existence it had been defined on 24 September 1993. I can remember where I was when Juan Antonio Samaranch uttered 'Syd-er-nee!' to announce that Australia's largest city had won the right to host the 2000 Olympics. I was part of the throng for a near-dawn breakfast function at a prominent Newcastle city hotel when the place erupted with the announcement. As a fringe-dweller of the sports media I allowed myself to dream about the possibility seven years down the track of working at the biggest event ever staged in Australia. It seemed a worthy goal.

In mid-1997 I was sitting underground at Teralba Colliery weighing up the options. We had two kids and one on the way, a mortgage and other debts. I knew I didn't want to be a miner for the rest of my life but the prospect of stepping outside the security of a guaranteed income, sick leave, paid annual holidays and retirement benefits into the unknown was scary. My casual role for the ABC had netted a maximum of $15 000 pa – hardly enough to sustain us. Then chance prised open a window of opportunity. The mining company was offering voluntary redundancy. With some of my workmates shaking their heads in disbelief, I took the cash and quit the mine.

From the comfort of a weekly pay packet I was instantly out in the cold, cold world of freelance media. But I was determined to make it work. I hosted trivia nights, did guest speaking appearances, emcee roles for awards ceremonies, filled in for newspaper reporters on leave, wrote a weekly football column – whatever paid a buck to supplement the casual rates from the ABC. I earned $40 000 a year for the next two years, working relentlessly in the knowledge that if I didn't get out of bed each day and wasn't self-disciplined enough I'd earn nothing and life as we knew it would collapse around us.

In June 1999 there was movement at the station. ABC Newcastle needed a full-time sports reporter. The position was advertised internally and externally around the nation. My application was on the desk within forty-eight hours of the ad's appearance. For six months I worked in the position on an acting basis. At the end of the stretch I was interviewed and awarded the job. Ten years after volunteering on that afternoon at Manuka Oval, I had a full-time career in radio. Life was fast, creative, full and exciting. The hours were long, parties relentless, sleep an optional luxury. When it came to increasing the workload, I never said no.

September 1999 – the National Rugby League grand final, Melbourne versus St George-Illawarra. Surrounded by 109 000 spectators I was at ground level delivering sideline eye reports to our largest audience of the year; as close to the action as humanly possible, working for the ABC and getting paid for it. I had goose bumps. This is the Olympic Stadium, I reminded myself. I'm standing on the track where Cathy Freeman will run the 400. Twelve months from now, I will be right here at the opening ceremony for the Games of the new millennium.

That grand final was decided in epic circumstances, referee Bill Harrigan awarding a penalty try in the dying minutes as Melbourne completed a miraculous come-from-behind win. I was closest to the penalty incident and was called on to paint a word picture of exactly how the drama had unfolded. It was exciting and as challenging as live sports broadcasting can possibly be. Hours after we had signed off and packed up for the evening, the adrenalin was still surging like a torrent. There was no way we were going to bed on the closing night of the football season. We partied like it was 1999.

That summer delivered the shortest off-season in history as football programs around Australia kicked off early so the decks would be cleared by September when the Olympics came to town. We holidayed as a family at Coffs Harbour and I had just enough time to shake the sand out of my shoes before jumping back into the workload. My strategy was that if I was good enough and put in the hard toil, the opportunity to be picked for the ABC's Sydney 2000 team would present itself. Two months out from the Games, notification arrived via email from the ABC's Games boss, Alan Marks, that I had been handed one of the two remaining general reporters' jobs on the team. I was going to the Olympics.

2

HEAVEN AND HELL

Where am I? What's happening? I have no idea. Doors are slamming. That much I know. An engine fires up and the vehicle is moving. The police wagon begins the fifteen-minute journey from Broadmeadow to James Fletcher Psychiatric Hospital. The hunched, dishevelled figure in the back has no concept of where he is going let alone the nature of the trip. Time is warping, buckling, stretching out of shape until a quarter of an hour will seem like an eternity. In my timeless capsule the growing impression that everything is fine, life is wonderful and that I am on my way to Heaven gathers strength like a sunrise firing up a new day. Visions of familiar faces and the warm sound of their voices buoy me onward and upward. We're all dead,

I affirm to myself, but that doesn't matter now because this updraft of gold-tinged euphoria is bearing me on to paradise.

Whup!

With the jolting violence of a high-voltage switch, my mood zaps from warm light to pure black. The glimpse of paradise is gone in a blink as I'm plunged into the darkest pit any night-terror could possibly conceive. The depression is all-consuming. Why? *Because you have killed yourself, Craig; you have committed suicide and for this terrible sin you are on your way to Hell!* With this awful realisation comes intolerable physical pain. My entire body is wracked with it as if I am being pummelled, twisted and wrenched by a gang of assailants. This torture confirms the obvious: I have been so bad – *so evil* – I have lived such a trashy existence that Hell is my certain destination. I am the very essence of evil, and I am on my way to discovering what Hell is really like. To me, this is no fantasy; this is absolutely real. I have entered the most terrifying moments of my existence – and it has only just begun.

Whup!

The switch has been thrown again. At something beyond warp speed I am back in the rapture of nirvana where clear light and golden warmth embrace me like a pair of loving arms and, with even greater blissful intensity than before, bear me smoothly towards paradise. This second taste of ecstasy confirms to me that the suicide notion was no more than a joke – everything is really okay; I am not such a bad guy and, to confirm that, here I am, securely, lovingly, on course to Heaven. *Phew!* I rock with laughter and relief at having been caught out by the joke and –

Whup!

It wasn't a joke! I'm instantly back in that terrible pit, only this time deeper and more agonising than before. The torture is relentless, terrifying, and there is no escape from the excruciating pain wracking my entire being. This is the ultimate confirmation: I have indeed killed myself by jumping in front of a train, abandoned my family and caused them irreparable pain and suffering. *'You bastard!'* I am screaming. *'How could you do this to your family?'* For this there is eternal torment.

Whup!

Whup!

Whup!

Like a super-energised neutron, I am oscillating between these two poles: Bliss and Hell. Each high is higher than the previous one; each low darker and deeper still. The emotional extremes are tearing me apart, body and soul. *I am stark, raving mad.*

To the police officers riding up front it must be apparent that they have a seriously ill individual in their keep. They hear peals of laughter and take a look through the view-panel to see their charge, seated in the back, rocking in euphoric delight. In an instant that mood is replaced by screams of agony as he throws himself off the seat and, shouting gibberish, thrashes around on the floor of the van.

The eastern philosophers tell us the greatest battle is with ourselves. A civil war is raging at the very core of my being. Here are the absolute highs and lows of psychosis and they are coming thick and fast. I am undergoing a psychotic experience of the highest order. I am so detached from reality that time and my actual surrounds have no relevance. *This is not a nightmare; this is Hell.*

Whup!

There are bright lights, TV cameras, I hear voices whispering and giggling. I know what this is: it is a test to see if I can keep every secret and confidence entrusted to me in the past thirty-seven years. But it is all happening before an audience. I realise the lights and cameras are there for an episode of *This Is Your Life* and I am the special guest. The fame I've always sought is about to be bestowed upon me. The venue is the Olympic Stadium and the audience comprises every famous person I've ever admired or known. The stands are packed with 100 000 people and billions are watching worldwide. This is as good as it gets! I'm laughing. I'm dead and so is every other soul in the stadium because this is how we're going to get to Heaven. But there is something wrong. The world is about to be destroyed in the aftermath of a nuclear war and anybody not at the stadium – Louise, our kids and all our families – will be destroyed in the fallout.

Firm hands have me in their hold. I am being lifted from the van. Suddenly, not alone anymore, I recognise the brutal mood swings have ceased. My next realisation is of being seated on a chair. For the first time since the railway station I notice my hands are cuffed behind my back. The room is sparsely furnished. Seated in a semicircle before me are seven people, all studying me intently. *I know what they're doing.*

In reality, as mental health professionals they are observing me to see what symptoms I display to determine whether I am a danger to myself or others as a prelude to scheduling me as a patient under the Mental Health Act.

'I know what you're doing,' I begin, reviving the foul-mouthed belligerent character from the railway platform. 'We're all fuckin' dead, so let's cut through the bullshit and get on with the job.'

One of them responds. Later, I would learn his name – Justin Bergholcs. I would also learn he is a psychiatric nurse and a member of Australia's Buddhist community who spends one half of each year working in mental health and the other on missions in places like Burma, Nepal and Tibet, setting up educational and medical services.

'No, Craig,' he says evenly. 'We're not dead. You're at James Fletcher Hospital; you've been brought here from Broadmeadow railway station and we're going to look after you.'

This is met with another volley of abuse. 'Look, I know where we are,' I say dismissively. 'We're in purgatory. We're all in purgatory and someone's going to decide whether we go up or down.'

Removed from the Heaven–Hell poles I'd encountered in the back of the police van, I had to come up with another explanation. We are somewhere between the two: purgatory. I am no longer euphoric or terrified. I have rediscovered my anger.

The first stage of the assessment concluded, despite my hostility and resistance, I am lifted from the chair and placed on a bed, exactly the same sort you'd find at your local GP's. I'm face-down, my trousers are lowered, I feel the quick jab of a needle and the surge of its contents. Soullessly, the powerful sedative does its work. High-voltage current sinks to muted pulse. Sometime after five o'clock on that frenzied afternoon, the mad beast is at last quiet. Asleep.

———

Louise had followed the police car to James Fletcher and had waited in dreadful apprehension in Admissions while I was assessed. With her husband asleep, she had the chance to speak with members of my assessment team. It was too early for an official diagnosis but it was during their conversation that the words 'Craig is displaying symptoms of bipolar disorder' were mentioned for the first time.

I wake at 11 pm. I had expended enough energy to sleep for a night and a day but the manic life-force at the heart of my psychosis has won its personal battle over the sedative. The handcuffs are gone. So are my belt and shoelaces. My confused gaze takes in the room, noting the absence of furniture and fittings, with the exception of the bed. The only feature interrupting the uniformity of the four white walls is a securely locked door. I'm in a cell.

A faltering self-appraisal reveals skin off elbows and knees, clothes filthy, torn in places, buttons missing. My media pass is gone. The perfect image of the Olympic dream is looking rather tattered.

What the hell has happened here? I ask myself, confused but calm. I was on my way to the Olympics and I wake up in a padded cell . . . I need to make a call.

The nursing staff escort me to an extension and patch me through to my home number. It's 11.30 pm, close to the end of the longest day of her life, when Louise picks up the phone.

'What's going on?' I want answers.

She is obviously upset; but in that calm, professional voice that nurses can effect when life as we know it has gone to Satan in a shopping trolley, my darling wife takes a deep breath and says: 'Craig, you became psychotic at the railway station; you were out of control, yelling and abusing Chris Williams. No-one could calm you down, so we called the Mental Health crisis team who suggested we call the police. The police came, saw the way you were behaving and they decided you needed to be in hospital. And that's where you are.'

Under the circumstances, Louise was fantastic. In truth, she could have been falling to pieces at the end of the phone, but how was I to know? As at the railway station, she had gone into professional nurse, rather than wife, mode. God knows how much more frightening it might have been for her had she not previously encountered psychosis in her working life.

My confusion at this point is still almost total. There are so many questions but Louise has the right words. As if talking to a little boy she says gently but firmly: 'Look, you

23

go back to bed now; get some sleep and we'll talk about all of this tomorrow.'

I put my head down on the pillow. It is almost midnight. Utter exhaustion and the lingering effects of the sedative combine to slip the moorings, cast me adrift from the worst day of my life and ferry me softly off to sleep.

3

THE DAYS AFTER

'Why do you think you are here, Craig?' The psychiatrist's voice is mellifluous and measured.

'Well, I'm here because I'm dead and you're interviewing me to find out where I best fit into the picture of the afterlife.'

It is about 8.30 am the next morning and a night's rest has failed to disabuse me of the conviction that I am deceased. My gentle inquisitor presses on with questions about my general health, injuries and blood type. He can't fool the crazy me. I know what he's after.

'You want to know what sort of specimen I am for my future role in the afterlife, don't you?'

'Craig, you are not dead; you are at James Fletcher

Hospital. In fact, at about ten o'clock your wife will be here to visit you and then you will see that you are still very much alive.'

Ten o'clock comes and goes. Ten-thirty. There is no sign of Louise and I take this as proof positive that I am dead – as dead as the Monty Python parrot. Eleven. As the time ticks by with no appearance from my wife, I remind everybody that they were wrong and I was right. 'Told you,' I say. 'She can't get to where I am.'

I am out of my padded cell for the day and in a communal area with about five other patients, all inmates of the high-security Waratah Wing. With staff out-numbering patients by about three to one, there are plenty to tell. 'Told you,' I repeat.

An announcement: 'Craig, your wife is here to see you.'

This place is like Fort Knox. Out through a set of security doors, down a corridor to a common room and, miracle of miracles, there she is. Louise. This is not an apparition. She is real and I know in an instant that I am indeed alive. This is blessed confirmation. I have died and I have come back to life. The proof is irrefutable: I *am* Jesus Christ! All bets are back on. I'm going to put this little hiccup behind me and get on with my mission to go to the Sydney Olympics and spread my message to the world. Eager to resume my Games project, I kiss Louise goodbye.

Let's take a small detour here to explain what's going on inside my scrambled head. The psychosis is only twenty-four hours old and, although the sedative and a night's sleep may have smoothed the mania's wild outer edges, it is still running like the Hunter River in the '55 flood. I'm trying to rationalise all the events befalling me but my jumbled thought processes are firing off illogical conclusions. I'm still crazy.

I need disciples. Just like Randall McMurphy in *One Flew Over the Cuckoo's Nest* rounding up fellow inmates for his fishing expedition, I'm busy recruiting patients and staff to accompany Jesus on my mission to the Olympics. The only difference here is that I'm way crazier than that feisty misfit McMurphy. My grandiose plans are still in place. I no longer have my media pass but that doesn't matter – I'm Jesus Christ, I'll simply walk across Homebush Bay to Olympic Stadium.

My fellow patients are an interesting collection. The bloke I notice first by virtue of his frenzied activity is in his mid-sixties. His wiring has become so fused he seems to be operating on maximum current all the time. He has no off-switch. His days are spent relentlessly circling the room talking to everybody, looking for a pair of us to take him on at two-handed 500. I'm not well enough to play him one hand at a time but his brilliant, overloaded mind needs such an outlet – anything to soak up the coursing energy.

By contrast, it is wise to avoid eye contact with the middle-aged woman. Left to her own devices she is, at best, surly. But any glance in her direction is met by a stream of abuse and the warning not to look at her, keep your distance. My guess is that the big guy with the beard is the wrong side of thirty. He admits himself to James Fletcher whenever he perceives the demons are about to call. God is his strength

27

and he declares this at every opportunity in a voice loud enough to stop a freight train. He's given me his solid assurance he will join me on the tour to the Olympics. The fifth occupant of Waratah Wing is an elderly gent, possibly suffering from dementia and depression. He is frail, has a European accent and keeps very much to himself.

Standing in the middle of the room, I take in these poor souls and, as addled as I am, a deep-seated prejudice swims up through the bilge water of my psyche and bobs to the surface. 'These people are seriously crazy,' says my prejudice on breaching. Then I look at myself. A change of clothes into T-shirt, track pants and a pair of slippers cannot disguise the fact that I am just like the other four: *I am in here too!*

Hey, I'm doing it tough here. I am in this place because I belong here. (Looking back, I realise this is the first hint some semblance of sanity was returning.)

A soul needs friends in a place like this, and I have three. Their names are Serenace, Epilim and Cogentin – my daily doses of medication. My unholy trinity. Serenace (Haloperidol) is used to treat chronic psychotic disorders and the manic phase of manic depression, while Epilim is used to treat epilepsy and mania and is particularly effective in patients with a rapid cycling pattern of manic illness. Cogentin, normally used as an anti-Parkinsonism treatment, is along for the ride because it offsets one of the less flattering side effects of Serenace: grimacing and contortions of the face, which can take on the appearance of lockjaw. Before the antidote takes effect I'll have twenty-four hours with my jaw seemingly rusted in place.

On day two or three (I don't remember which) this facial grimacing coincides with a visit from two of my best cricketing mates, Wayne Fowler and Peter Schacht. Wayne and I had played in opposing clubs and, as two all-rounders of similar ability, were natural rivals who became great mates. The friendship was consolidated on a 1985 Newcastle Cavaliers tour of England and Wales – thirty-one days with plenty of cricket topped off with lashings of hospitality. Peter wasn't on that trip but for ten summers with the Belmont club he kept wicket to my bowling and was a great lower-order batsman. After cricket, the Fowler and Schacht families remained among our closest friends.

They arrive at James Fletcher together and are shown into a small courtyard in the Waratah Wing where the three of us take our seats. By now the Jesus delusion has shifted and I understand who I am, that I am seriously ill and won't be going to the Olympics just yet. The two visitors are trying to put on a brave face but are failing miserably. The high-security nature of the surrounds has obviously thrown them. My demeanour doesn't help. I'm doing my best to explain why I am here rather than in Sydney, but the lockjaw is strangling the delivery and eliciting a range of facial contortions that would be absolutely hilarious if this wasn't so bloody serious. The more I persist the worse it looks and sounds.

Try saying the following without moving your bottom jaw or lips and you'll have an idea: 'Boys, don't worry, I'm okay. The only reason I'm talking like this is because of the side effects of the medication they've given me.'

29

Peter and Wayne must have been beside themselves. Thankfully, over the next couple of days the antidote kicks in and movement returns to the jaw. The downside to the antidote is that it blurs my vision.

On day four I am transferred out of the Waratah Wing into a lower-security Acacia ward. I have come down from the stratospheric heights of the mania and note that the guy in the bed next to me is suffering serious delusions. When he is well enough, we swap stories. 'Three days ago,' I tell him, 'I was Jesus Christ.'

He near pisses himself laughing. Then he tells me he was Superman and had flown into hospital. We both laugh. This is about as bleak as humour gets, but if laughter is the best medicine here are two loons self-medicating at their own expense. His plight is a mirror of my own. He is your average bloke in the same situation as me.

Diagonally to my left is a poor soul admitted for deep depression. He is a big man, in his mid-twenties and a lovely individual. He desperately wants to get better and determines to engage himself in the occupational therapy and organised activities like lawn bowls, craft and cooking. But, when the time comes, he cannot move. He lies there like a sad hulk stuck fast on a mudbank, trapped in perpetual gloom.

The other occupant of our ward is seriously deluded. He has a picture of a prominent Australian female vocalist and assures us she is coming to visit him tonight. His stories are spectacular and his grip on reality totally nonexistent.

Activity is important in the rehabilitation process. We

play cricket and tennis and cook carrot cakes. We eat together in a communal room. On the Friday, the television in the communal room shows the opening ceremony at the Olympics.

A steady stream of family and close friends continues to visit. Mum is holidaying in the UK, catching up with relatives, and has been given a diluted version of events. It's just as well. By the time she returns the eye of the cyclone will have come and gone. At the end of the first week, my father Dick Hamilton arrives with my sister Kate. Of all the people doing their level best to cope with the news that a loved one has wound up on the wrong side of the nuthouse walls, Kate was not faring very well at all. It was understandable. Six years my junior, she had always looked up to me as her big brother, guiding light and the rock to cling to throughout life's squalls. Suddenly, the confidant, the ever-reliable edifice, had been shown to have feet of clay.

Kate lived on a small farm at Whittingham near Single-ton and to Louise's brother Graham had fallen the difficult task of driving out to tell her the news. Graham would later relate that Kate was extremely upset. On arriving with Dad, she is mightily relieved to see that her brother is functioning – not on all cylinders, but he isn't as bad as she may have feared. It is just as well she didn't see me on day one. It's been a stormy week but the drugs have stabilised the ship. The morning medication ritual is doing its job. Plastic-cup-by-tiny-plastic-cup-of-pills I'm getting a little better each day. My three chemical crewmates – Cogentin, Sere-nace and Epilim – trimming the sails, adjusting the ballast, navigating a way out of the shoals. Vaulting optimism tells me I'm right back on course to a full recovery. *There's no reason why I can't be at the Olympics next week.*

When faced with the unspeakable, we all have a need to believe that everything is indeed okay. As parents, we are programmed to look for the best in our children. My dad seized on this optimism and relayed it to his sister, my Auntie June. Now, not only do I have no understanding of just how sick I am, neither does my dad. Putting Humpty Dumpty back together is not just a matter of gluing the eggshell – first you have to unscramble the egg!

If I'm disappointed at missing the opening ceremony, I'm more than compensated by my conviction that I'll be in Sydney for week two of the great event. Four days of rest, medication and occupational therapy have worked the minor miracle of my carers agreeing to allow me home for a day visit on the weekend. This is great news. The kids know I haven't gone to Sydney and have been able to visit me in hospital. Perhaps used to their dad being away on work commitments, they appear largely untroubled by the events of the week. But as I try to relax in the bosom of my family, it becomes apparent that Josh, our eldest, is not letting me out of his sight. At nine, he is well past the clingy stage yet it is very apparent, particularly to an ever-vigilant Louise, that he wants to share my chair, needs more hugs than usual and is seeking reassurance.

The day goes uneventfully until, on the way back to the hospital, Louise relates how she was landed with the task of divesting Dad of his optimism. She recounts how her father-in-law said: 'Gee, Craig's coming along. It's great news – he's off to the Olympics next week.'

'Dick, Craig is not going to the Olympics next week,' Louise said. 'Craig is not going to the Olympics at all. He is very sick. In fact, he's not going to be at work for months.' It was the cold, hard left hook of reality. He was taken aback. But whatever impact it had on Dad, his shock could not have been greater than mine.

'But I'm feeling better,' I splutter, 'why can't I go?'

There was no way of sugar-coating this: 'No, it's over. You're not going.'

It was a hard message. I needed to hear it. This was the stamp of finality. I was not going to the Olympics. Full-stop.

With an acceptance that it isn't meant to be and a recognition that I'm not well enough to be there, I keep a casual eye on the Olympics coverage as my stay extends into week two. Every day I am feeling better. Once again, thoughts can come and go with the easy motion of surf lapping at the shore. No longer do they transmute into outrageous delusions. With each slow ebb and flow of the tide I can feel my consciousness moving surely back to a familiar harbour. It is early days, but I am starting to rejoin my old self.

Part of our therapy involves a group forum where patients come together with a few of our carers for an 'expression' session. We take it in turn to address the group, telling them who we are, where we come from, a little about ourselves and what we intend to do today. Ten days or so after my admission, I'm invited to open the batting in one of these sessions. By now, my sense of humour has returned.

'My name is Jesus Christ,' I begin. 'I come from a small place – you might have heard of it – it's called Nazareth, and my job today is to save the world.'

While most of the patients had blank looks on their faces, the staff broke up laughing. I guess it was my way of saying: 'I understand I have a long way to go, but I'm on the way to recovery, and at least I'm well enough to have a good laugh at myself.'

I was discharged the next day.

At home I was going stir-crazy with the desire to throw myself back into activity. Work presented the obvious outlet and my mind was cantering in that direction. The ABC had been very supportive throughout my crisis but like any employer it is bound by a duty-of-care. After having suffered such a trauma I would be obliged to appear before an independent psychiatrist to be assessed as to my fitness to return to work. In the fullness of time, it would take not one but three separate sessions with psychiatrists before I received the green light to resume my career.

From where I was standing, my ultimate recovery could have been just over the next sand dune. Hope springs eternal. The long view would reveal I had a thousand dunes to traverse before I could walk out of this desert. The journey in had taken at least a year. It would take that length of time again to find a way out. I could start by retracing my footsteps – from the beginning.

4

FARM BOY, MINER, MARRIED MAN

Maureen and Dick Hamilton's firstborn was a boy who came kicking into the world at Singleton Hospital in the Upper Hunter district of New South Wales on 21 January 1963. They christened me Craig and took me home to be raised on our modest dairy farm on the outskirts of the town.

The Hamiltons were pioneering stock, farmers by instinct and tradition. In the 1840s Isaiah Hamilton left County Monaghan for New South Wales, arriving with his family in the Hunter, where they purchased land at Glendonbrook near Singleton. They cleared what the cedar-getters hadn't already taken and let their dairy herds loose on the verdant slopes and river flats of a property they called 'Killyfuddy' after the farm they had left in Ireland.

Mum was a British nurse who had migrated in the early 1960s on the Commonwealth's Assisted Passage program – ten quid and a set of oars was the standing joke. A job in the local hospital brought Maureen to Singleton, where she made the acquaintance of one of the town's confirmed bachelors. Dick was a dairy farmer and the son of a dairy farmer who had also owned racehorses purchased with the profits from working the fertile farmlands of the Upper Hunter. Dad is a character and if he hadn't spent all his life running a farm he might have enjoyed a different existence pursuing life as 'a colourful racing identity'.

My brother Ian was born sixteen months after me. Four and a half years later came a daughter, our sister Kate. Christened Katherine, her two brothers always called her Katie and took on the role of her protectors like a second skin. While most other farm kids had to bus it to school from outlying areas, we lived close enough to town to be able to ride our bikes as soon as we were old enough. It was the best of both worlds – town and country.

From an early age we were aware of just how hard our parents worked. My paternal grandfather, also called Dick, had died when I was about four. Dad was the only son and had worked alongside his father since boyhood, only to see 'Killyfuddy' pass into the hands of an older sister and her husband. For many folk on the land, deeding the property to the eldest was an accepted alternative to breaking up the farm. Dad went to town to work odd jobs, did a bit of droving and eventually took on working 'Bebeah', a smaller dairy farm owned by my grandmother's brother, Leigh Dunford. Dick Hamilton made a good fist of running the property and when Leigh died, the farm was willed to my dad. The daily pre-dawn start and the regular demands of milking left little time for a social life, which explained why Dick remained a confirmed bachelor well into his thirties.

I watched my dad work that farm for twenty years without taking so much as a single sick day. Thrown by a horse, he suffered a broken pelvis but rather than head for bed, he phoned a neighbour to help with the milking. Propped up on a stick, Dick Hamilton supervised from the middle of the yard, waving his crutch at any recalcitrant cows. When I was about twelve, Dad made his regular Wednesday trip to town for the Singleton sales. By six that evening we guessed he had been caught up with mates at the Royal Hotel knocking back a few beers. With no sign of him and the cows needing to be milked, Ian, aged ten, and I tackled the job. The old man rolled in about eight, muttering about how the cows needed milking.

'It's already done,' we told him.

'What?' he said in disbelief. 'I'll have to go and check.'

He jumped on the tractor, motored down to the yards and then drove straight back to the Royal where he announced: 'They've milked the bloody cows!' and promptly shouted the bar.

As kids we were expected to pull our weight on the farm, to muck in and lend a hand. We didn't exactly relish the workload but I can't recall a single instance when our chores denied us a social or sporting opportunity. At times we envied the town kids and their lifestyle, only to learn that all they ever wanted to do was get out on a farm and dive into the country life.

There was an underlying sense that we weren't the richest kids in that neck of the woods but we never wanted for anything. When I was sixteen, Mum and Dad scraped up the cash to send me on a schoolboy rugby tour of New Zealand. Our parents encouraged us to play sport and Ian had followed me into cricket and rugby with local teams. In half a lifetime of competitive sport, I would encounter no greater rivalry than those backyard sessions with Ian. It didn't matter whether it was cricket or football, when brother faced off against brother, it was on.

Junior school was the Hunter Street Public School and my secondary years were spent at Singleton High in unremarkable adolescent harmony. It was a very typical upbringing in a typical country community of regional Australia.

Like many families we experienced our share of tensions on the home front. During my teenage years our parents separated for a couple of weeks on two occasions but managed to bury their differences and keep the family together. In those days before counselling was so readily available, couples simply internalised their pain and got on with the job of raising the kids. The spark seemed to be Dad's partiality for a drink. When he arrived home late after a session in town, he was known to get pretty loud and angry, but never violent.

In those days before random breath testing and awareness programs, drinking to excess was almost an accepted part of Australian regional life. Our experience certainly wasn't untypical. Many kids started drinking early. At fifteen, I was a late beginner – smashed on four cans of beer at a mate's birthday party and backing up the next weekend for another dose. By sixteen, both Ian and I were confident enough to walk into a pub and order a beer knowing that nobody would show us the door. Mum's uncle had been an alcoholic; she had seen the worst of alcohol abuse during her nursing years and strongly opposed our under-age drinking. Dad didn't see it as such a huge problem. If I had a hangover after a heavy Friday night, the old man would say, 'Get a glass of Eno's into you.' Five minutes later I'd be out the back throwing up.

As the golden stretch of school days neared its end, I had no idea about a choice of career. The farm was definitely not an option. I had seen Dad bust his back 365 days a year; up in the morning to milk the herd, work all day and then milk them again in the afternoon. A ball and chain. Planning something as basic as a weekend away or a daytrip to the coast was a major logistical exercise. We rarely had a family holiday. Dad loved the work but it denied him so many choices in life. He could never walk away. My father's lot had convinced me that I'd never choose a career which would entrap me seven days a week. Like the people in town, I wanted a job that offered at least two days off and holidays as well.

A newspaper cutting pinned to the Year 12 noticeboard

at school advertised traineeships with BHP Collieries. In 1980, the coalmining industry was booming. Prices were healthy and demand was high. There were good salaries and bonuses on offer. By my dad's standards, work hours were short and holidays generous. As a career, mining didn't exactly inspire me but there was no way I could have gone back to the farm, put my feet up and waited for a career to roll through the gate and ferry me off to a life of ease and prosperity.

In the winter of 1980 I travelled down the valley to the coastal site of John Darling Colliery to be interviewed by Cliff Marsh (Manager – Personnel, BHP Collieries) and his off-sider Dick Maclean. Scholastically, my credentials weren't great but Cliff was taken by my sporting qualifications, particularly my happy knack of being chosen captain of most teams in which I had played. At the time, I had no way of knowing that Cliff Marsh was a sporting institution in the coastal areas of Newcastle and Lake Macquarie. A celebrated administrator, he was involved across a range of sports, particularly surf lifesaving – he was to become a life member of the national association. Later, he would oversee the Westpac Rescue Helicopter operation in our region. Despite the age difference, we struck up a natural rapport from the first handshake and remain great friends today.

English was the first paper for the Higher School Certificate of 1980. The next morning, a letter arrived from BHP Collieries advising that I had been granted a cadetship. I sat the remaining subjects knowing that my immediate job prospects were secure. Any pressure I had felt to excel in the exams evaporated with the reading of that letter. My marks reflected my relaxed attitude, the best result being English, the paper I had sat the day before the letter arrived.

On 5 January 1981, a couple of weeks shy of my eighteenth birthday, I reported for work at Stockton Borehole Colliery. Cliff Marsh's eye for sporting ability was at least consistent. Starting with me was Grant Rodgers of Hamilton Rugby Club, Wallsend Cricket Club and a team-mate of mine from the Combined High Schools representative cricket side. It was the beginning of another lifelong friendship. Paul Murphy, a first grade soccer player with the Highfields Azzurri club, completed the trio of cadets to start at Stockton Borehole that day. In all, fifteen cadets had been chosen for that year's intake with three assigned to each of BHP's five mines in the Lower Hunter. Over a two-year period we were obliged to work at all five collieries on a rotating basis, learning everything we could about below-ground mining. We would graduate from the process as mine deputies.

The excitement of new adventure bore me into the cage in the company of a bunch of helmeted strangers for my first trip underground. Stepping out of that coop far below the surface was a huge shock, particularly for a farm boy raised in the wide open spaces. It was dark, cramped, dusty and damp in many places – a totally alien environment. Welcome to the workforce, Craig.

In those days before it was negotiated away, mining companies still observed the tradition of employing the sons of miners. The new intake of cadets certainly didn't fit that family mould. We were outsiders. But, allowing for a bit of cheeky banter, our welcome was cordial.

Farmwork had been hard yakka, but mining was something else again. There was no doubt that when they interviewed a job applicant they were weighing up his aptitude to handle this physically confronting environment. Coming from the farm and having played plenty of sport, I was in good shape. But, not quite eighteen, I was still more boy than man and had a bit of growing to do.

On that first day we were taken on a tour of the mine by the under-manager in charge, Norm Ward. He was a coalminer from his helmet to his boot-heels, an experienced, knowledgeable and hard-nosed leader who took crap from nobody. It was a reality check. Norm's message was: 'Boys, you're in a dangerous place, keep your wits about you, look after your mates, safety is paramount.' It was a perfect introduction from a singularly impressive bloke. If Norm guessed he had won our respect, he wasn't going to let it get in the way of his tendency to assign us some terrible jobs.

I'd been there a few years, done the round of the pits and returned to Stockton Borehole when we were required to sink a linking airshaft between two seams that sat one above the other separated by about 10–12 metres of solid rock. It had already been raise-bored, which meant a team had drilled a hole down from the top; then, working from the bottom seam to the top, cut the shaft to a diameter of about a metre. Our job was to extend that metre out to

42

about six to make it a full-sized airshaft. We were hanging from harnesses over this abyss, working with pneumatic drills to create shot-holes for inserting explosives around the perimeter. The din of machinery in the confined space resonated through every molecule of your being. The draft from below was blasting up at us with the ferocity of a jet engine. As we dislodged mud and stone and pushed it into the hole, the updraft caught any loose material and blew it into our faces, like a constantly erupting volcano. There was no respite. It continued nonstop for the entire shift, day after day, week after week. Our industrial award allowed for dirt or water money, an extra $1.80 a day, but it was never a given. I'd have to front Norm and ask for it. To test the veracity of the claim he would reach across his desk and rub a thumb down a grime-caked face before muttering: 'Yeah, all right.' He wasn't about to cut us any slack.

Down the track my mates would give me flak about earning the then handsome wage of $750 a week for working down a mine. They thought it must have been a great lurk collecting that much money for doing who knows what. My response was that it was a rough old place to work and we earned every cent. They didn't believe me so I laid on a guided tour for Chris Williams, Peter Schacht, Tom Hoppe and Alan Sharp. It opened their eyes in more ways than one. They had no idea of the confined spaces, dust and dark. Until you put your hand centimetres from your face and still can't see it, you have no idea how deathly dark it is down there. Where the machines are working the noise is unbelievable. And, it's a dangerous

43

place. You have to watch your back, sides and front as well as your workmates. When we made it back to the surface even the most cynical of the boys was singing a different tune. 'You wouldn't get me down there for two grand a week,' was the summation.

Alan Cooper was a genial Scot who came to Australia to win soccer premierships with the famous Coalfields team, the Weston Bears. When he wasn't thrilling locals with dribbling runs down the wing, Coop worked below ground as an electrician. Although his playing days were long gone he was still deeply involved with his beloved Weston when I joined the workforce at Stockton Borehole where his reputation as nature's gentleman had preceded him. You'd never meet a nicer bloke. Coop's change basket – the place where we hung our street clothes – was only a couple of positions away from mine, so we'd see each other on a daily basis.

Coop was the electrician on the longwall miner when one day the armoured-face conveyor – a continuous loop of steel chain which runs the cut coal out to a junction point – became jammed by a large rock. Coop grabbed a seven-pound hammer and started swinging at the rock to clear it. Of course, the conveyor should have been shut off but, in the interests of keeping production flowing, taking such risks was common. Swinging the sledge in the confined space, he lost his footing and was pulled into the hammers of the crusher. It's the worst nightmare for an underground miner. The injuries he incurred defy description. The machinery was stopped but they couldn't get him out.

First-aid was administered as the emergency call went out for paramedics and the rescue helicopter. It might have been forty minutes or more before they got to him and they had to cut the machinery apart with oxy gear to free his broken body. By the time they got Coop to the pit top he had died.

The blokes who worked with him that day had no counselling. We had a day off in his memory and then it was straight back to work. Some blokes never got over it. I was deeply troubled by it and spoke to my dad, who advised me to attend the funeral. They played the pipes for Coop. It was very moving. You can find his name inscribed on the memorial wall to the mining dead.

The inherent danger of the workplace breeds great camaraderie and a tough-minded sense of humour. The worst thing you could have down the pit was a thin skin. If the blokes spotted you were sensitive to a bit of a ribbing, look out. It's a tough environment.

My roughest time below ground was the months we spent creating a single entry for a longwall. By definition it was a one-way road – one way in and the same way out. The aim was to define a block of coal a couple of kilometres long by about 200 metres wide. As this roadway of a couple of kilometres or so was being bored, inexplicably it started taking weight. That's mining terminology for the fact that it was starting to collapse. The roadway had already been bolted with seven-foot bolts totally encased in chemical resin with W-straps strung to form a solid cocoon. The walls too had been bolted and plated to hold the place together. Yet, it was clear it wasn't holding. Under most circumstances you'd get the hell out of there. But this block of coal was the future of the mine; without it we didn't have jobs. So, they brought contractors in to cable-bolt the roof for extra support, and we installed a row of supporting timber posts as thick as power poles a metre apart down the length of one wall leaving just enough room for a transport to pass.

Around-the-clock-shifts were rostered to set those posts and we'd arrive at work to see these huge pieces of timber we had installed the day before busted and bent like matchsticks. We didn't know it at the time, but we were underneath another seam which had previously been mined and was throwing weight onto the seam below. The roof was coming in but nobody was willing to quit. It was horrendous. How somebody wasn't killed on the roadway I'll never know. There were roof falls but fortunately they missed everybody. We had broken limbs and so many other injuries but we didn't lose anybody. The work continued under those conditions for months. You could see the stress taking its toll on the blokes – we didn't discuss it above ground or at home because any sensible person wouldn't have let us go back down.

They brought out an expert on 'rough territory' – that's bad geological conditions – from the United States to solve our problems. He had an international reputation as a troubleshooter who had been able to extract machinery from some of the worse situations in US mines. He walked the two kilometres of the roadway, noting the busted timber and buckling roof. When he reached the end he said: 'Pull the gear out; you can't keep that road open.' As the inspection party turned to walk back down the roadway, the American said: 'I'm not walking out that way, it's too dangerous.' He cut across the coalface and used the only other way out, through the tailgate. Now, this bloke had seen it all and he refused to walk back down the road we'd been working on for months. Yep, it was a dangerous place.

——

With the mines more than an hour's drive from the farm, I teamed up with Brian Cullen and Bob Wilson, two other young blokes who had never lived away from home before, to rent a flat in suburban Newcastle. We had all come from homes where beds were mysteriously made each day and the dishes must have washed themselves. What a shock it was to return to the flat each evening to find the beds still unmade and a mountain of dirty crockery sitting in the kitchen sink. Drastic action had to be taken. And it was. We avoided the kitchen at all costs and dined at Wallsend RSL – cutlets and three vegies for $6.00. As for the beds, we never quite figured that one out. If the flat was a dump when we moved in, the new inhabitants didn't exactly convert it into reality TV's dream makeover. There were holes in the couches, piles of magazines propped up wonky furniture and we never really made the acquaintance of vacuum cleaner or floor mop. We had the domestic instincts of the flatmates of that 1980s British comedy classic *The Young Ones*. I was there only three nights a week so maybe my turn on the cleaning roster fell on the days I was back in Singleton.

Sport was one good reason for regular returns to my home town. The other was Louise Kelly. Cricket had been our point of introduction: her dad Pat and I were team-mates. Pat Kelly was one of those mainstays of local sport central to every country town. A natural leader and talented all-rounder, he had been an inspirational rugby league player who had captained and coached Singleton to a pre-miership. Our paths crossed when he joined Glendon Cricket Club in the district competition. Pat became the first grade captain and I was one of his young bowlers. He was a man to be respected. When he played cricket his four kids – Louise, Christine, Graham and Matthew – turned up to support the team.

Louise and I went out together for the first time in December 1980. We've been an item ever since. When she left school in 1982 and moved down to Newcastle to start nursing at the Mater Hospital in suburban Waratah, my trips back to Singleton became less frequent. Time and dis-tance would finally cut the playing ties with the Glendon gang. Instead, a workmate, Stephen Brown, invited me to train with his club. Former New South Wales wicketkeeper Kerry Thompson, the captain and coach of Belmont, made me very welcome and by the spring of 1983, I was testing my bowling arm against the best batsmen in the Newcastle district competition.

Mine was so typical of the life of any working boy making his way in the world. It was a time of shared houses, organised sport, a secure income and the company of a wonderful girl. With a good mix of Singleton people in Newcastle for university, teachers college and nursing, we never felt homesick. Whether it was new friends or the gang from our home town, there was always a group of us ready to hit the pub and club scene at least once a week to catch a live band. This time had a soundtrack all of its own: pub rock. Like tiny restaurant servings and other less redeeming fads of the 1970s–80s, disco never quite took a hold in plain-speaking Newcastle. Instead of turntables and djs, the pub and club scene fairly pumped with talented local bands and the best touring acts. We had countless great nights at the Shortland Hotel near Newcastle uni, catching the Musical Flags, featuring Steve Abbott aka The Sandman. After a scorching afternoon of cricket, there was no better way to unwind on a Saturday evening than with a few beers and a big belt of Cold Chisel, Australian Crawl or Richard Clapton.

I was sharing a house with John Horsley, Cathy Barlow and Ian Morrison when they insisted I join them to catch a band guaranteed to blow me away. Midnight Oil were raw, powerful, musically tight, came with lots of attitude and a social conscience, plus they didn't mind ruffling a few feathers. For the next fifteen years it became a ritual to catch the Oils whenever they came to town. Fuelled by bourbon and Coke, I'd be joined by Wayne Fowler, all six feet four inches of him, in the moshpit going toe-to-toe with Peter Garrett.

Despite the high energy of the pub-rock culture of the

eighties, there never seemed to be any trouble. We always made it home unscathed. For a beer-drinking, head-banging, blue-collar boy, this was rock 'n' roll heaven: those nights at the end of the sun-drenched days, aglow with beer and music, while Jimmy Barnes sang 'Forever Now'.

Louise and I became engaged and were wed in September 1987. A year later we bought our first home, the New Lambton house where we still live today. Life had found a blissful momentum and there seemed no reason anything could break its happy stride.

5

WINDING THE SPRING

For sports-crazed kids growing up in regional areas away from the commercial networks' fixation with capital city markets, the ABC was our link to the glamorous world of the Big Time. Country kids lolling in the shade of a gum waiting for their turn to bat would bend an ear to a car radio relaying the dulcet tones of Alan McGilvray, Norman May, Alan Marks and company with their ball-by-ball accounts from far-off Test matches. As we became more discerning we grew to appreciate the national broadcaster's passion for accuracy and detail, its culture of reliability, and its capacity to choose commentators with the gift of painting word pictures. She never played much Oils or Chisel, but Auntie was (and still is) the yardstick for credibility in sports entertainment.

My childhood dream had been to open the bowling for Australia just like my hero Dennis Lillee. I didn't even come close but wasn't disappointed because I'd at least given cricket and football my very best shot. The next best option was being paid to attend the big sporting events. This wish had come true: in June 1999 I was granted a full-time job with the national broadcaster as part of the ABC Sport team. Not even a wire brush could have removed the smile from my face.

The final year of the old millennium was a year of euphoria – a party year. Work was fantastic, the creative juices fairly gushed and I was riding my energy levels like a pro surfer hooking into the perfect swell. Nothing was too difficult, no job-load too great. Whatever request came into the office, my hand was up in a blink. The word 'no' wasn't in my lexicon. Part of the territory of having a media profile in a regional centre as opposed to a capital city is the call to host presentation nights, make guest speaking appearances, and be involved in charity work, fundraisers and civic events. Most of this work is unpaid and seen as a civic contribution. After all, these people are your audience.

Before I arrived on the scene, local identities like Mike Rabbitt and Gary Harley would make hundreds of appearances a year for community causes. People might have seen Mike reading the evening sports news on TV and thought: 'What an easy job!' What they didn't see was him criss-crossing the region, darting from one hosting commitment to the next corporate luncheon and then on to a charity do, day after day, night after night, forever upbeat, perpetually professional and friendly. For the audience sitting there over a meal waiting to be entertained, it can be an enjoyable evening. But for the host, it is work. It requires discipline, preparation and enough adrenalin to ensure you are constantly on your game. Few people had an insight as to how hard Mike worked. I admired him immensely. An indication of how stretched he was came with the frantic calls for me to stand in for him because he had been double-booked. If it happened once, it happened a dozen times. Pretty soon my book was almost as full as Mike's. You turn up at the venue, look around the room at the audience and the thought crosses your mind: 'I can turn this into a Dimboola. If I'm off my game tonight, this can be a disaster.'

Since my late teens I had been the nominated emcee for my club cricket and rugby functions; expanding this load to embrace the broader community didn't seem too much of a stretch for a man with my get-up-and-go. The terror associated with standing up and addressing an audience of 200 people had long been conquered. But the pressure to perform is always there. Beneath that stress is a panic underpinned by the unspoken question: 'When are they going to see through me? When are they going to see that I have the same frailties, weaknesses, insecurities and fears as they do? Once they do, the game is up. Just like in the *Wizard of Oz*, they'll pull the curtain aside and discover a frightened little man.' Each time somebody stands up and delivers a seamless public-speaking performance he has managed to subdue those demons. It's a great act. All of us who pull off the illusion that we are in control deserve an Oscar.

In this way, career became something larger than a regular forty-hour week. It dominated my existence. If there was a drink on after work, going home before midnight was not an option. Before 1999 and my full-time appointment, I was already burning the candle at both ends. Stepping out of a nightclub at five in the morning to go on-air at six seems like a crazy play, but it happened more than once. The Castle nightclub was about half a kilometre from the ABC studios. There I was on the footpath, blinking in the early morning light. My drinking pals headed home to bed and I strolled on down to work, plonked myself in the chair and, at ten past six, turned on the mike to say: 'Good morning, 1233 ABC Newcastle, you're with Craig Hamilton.' No-one was any the wiser. The energy levels would last an hour and by seven o'clock I was a shot duck, but still had three hours to go. At nine o'clock Lindy Burns walked into the studio and said: 'You stink of alcohol!'

'No wonder,' I responded, 'I've been drinking until five o'clock this morning!'

Nobody out there in radioland would have guessed. I managed to remain professional enough to hold it together. But, as for self-knowledge, even if I'd heard the alarm bells, I did not realise they were ringing for me.

Alcohol consumption was not a daily routine – perhaps it should have been. From my teenage years on, drinking was an intermittent rather than a regular pastime. The demands of training and performance steer athletes away from the casual drink in favour of a sizeable session at the weekend once the contest has been settled. My attraction to the pub-rock scene dictated a similar tempo – beer, bourbon and bands on a Saturday night. On reflection, it would have been better to have gone home at the end of each day like so many of my mining mates and relaxed with a beer or two. Instead, I'd save it all up for a binge session, stay out all night and consume enough beer to drown an elephant before switching to bourbon and obliterating a couple of hemispheres worth of brain cells.

This was an irregular occurrence – say, every couple of months – but when it happened, it was monumental. It was never planned that way; when alcohol hosed the inhibitions and the best intentions for an early night down the drain, I was lost to my own weaknesses. And so on it went, blundering every couple of months or so from one binge session to the next. I can recall dropping in on a buck's night with the full intention of staying long enough to be polite but, three venues and a damful of booze later, finding once again that I had outlasted them all. Melbourne Cup Day was always a big one. My regular gig was hosting a lunch at the Newcastle Workers Club. I'd never drink while working, but once the job was done, I'd kick on to all hours.

My motor was running fast, chewing up work and the social life at a voracious speed. Sleep was reduced to a few hours a night. With that much dynamism, who needed sleep? If somebody had paused to watch this whirling ball of energy they might have asked: how does he do it? Easy. I was a machine, or so I thought. The truth was I was running on a supernatural fuel that gave me fantastic power. But, like so much magic, there was a terrible downside to the deal – this gas would ultimately wreck the vehicle. Much later, I would learn the name of this rocket fuel: mania.

When you are in this state, it takes an awful amount of alcohol to knock the edge off it. You can throw down shots like the original booze brother but still remain upright and coherent. But there's always a trade-off: grog is a dreadful depressant and, in such quantities, will ultimately nail your liver to the wall. My hangovers would last for days.

It caused problems on the home front. While Louise was stuck at home caring for our babies, I was out socialising with my media contacts. Gone were the days when we regularly stepped out as a young couple. Between having kids and me embracing my new career, our social partnership had almost disappeared. Louise would ask what time I expected to be home and I might promise 'midnight' but on way too many occasions it was four or five. As often as not, my wife would be wide awake when I got home, a fusion of concern and cold fury. When I crawled in around dawn I'd always be apologetic, but the damage had been done. Out having a laugh, drink and a good time, it never occurred to me that somebody could be worrying about me.

The lessons of moderation and balance are timeless. I would have to learn them the hard way. Today, a casual beer is to be enjoyed. Save for a couple on my fortieth birthday, the bourbons are off the drinks list. I'm no teetotaller and definitely not a wowser, but 'moderation in all things' is a golden mantra. Striking a balance, allocating the appropriate time and energy for work, family and other commitments, is not easy. Today, I'm still wrestling with it.

Throughout the nineties, while I had a five-day-a-week job down the mine and was trying to expand my part-time media career into a full-time profession, I was working myself to death. Left with the entire family load to shoulder, it was particularly hard on Louise. The rationale was that this would be a temporary phase; Louise knew I didn't want to be a coalminer forever; the ABC or another broadcaster would eventually throw me a full-time gig and normality would return to our household. Well, in 1999 the ABC *had* signed me as a permanent fixture and normality *had not* returned at all. Only now can I see how much this must have concerned and exasperated my wife, particularly after February 1997 when the arrival of Laura had brought our brood to three.

Louise had taken maternity leave for the arrival of each of the kids and each time had returned to work on a part-time basis. Juggling child-rearing and the demands of a nursing career without the active support of a partner can't have been easy. It was a period which taught us the value of the extended family. Living an hour's drive away from our Singleton birthplace, we did not have the luxury of making a quick phone call to have a grandparent pop around to keep an eye on the kids or simply to be able to drop them off while we took care of a pressing appointment or grabbed much-needed downtime together. In my gung-ho state I was in no condition to identify just how much we needed the support of family and friends. A more measured soul might have taken stock of the situation and realised adjustments had to be made. That wasn't me. Any intro-spection on my part would have gone no further than saying, 'I'm just having a good time with work and life and, yes, I do enjoy a drink or two.'

Another by-product of this frantic life was the pile of speeding fines I racked up as my hectic pace zapped me from pillar to post with barely enough hours in the day to meet the crazy demands I had placed on myself. It was a time when my solicitor needed to be on call to preserve my driving licence and keep me on the road so that I could continue to work. Like a clockwork toy, the faster I went, the tighter I wound the spring.

6

NEW YEAR'S EVE, 1999

Had there ever been *such* a countdown to *such* a party? Starting with Sydney's spectacular fireworks display, an international live telecast will sweep a worldwide audience from city to city as Planet Earth rotates into a new day, a new year and a new millennium. For weeks we have been dazzled by descriptions of how the glitterati are planning to celebrate, the details of enough fireworks to blow the old millennium to kingdom come, the pageant of performers queuing to open their vocal chords and thrash their instruments in a rousing welcome to a new age, and the mountains of fine food and sea of champers we will consume at the worldwide party to end all parties.

Rather than on a luxury yacht or at a harbourside

penthouse apartment, we've gathered with close mates for a backyard bash. The venue is the home of our close friends Peter and Donna Schacht. Nursing drinks and chatting with the relaxed comfort of old associates are Wayne and Catherine Fowler, Tony and Louise Southward and a solid sample of our closest acquaintances. The observance of ritual binds us, cements friendships. As the music combines in familiar harmony with the happy tinkling of glass and laughter and rises up into the summer night, the elements fall easily into place for what should be the best of times.

It ain't, though. At least, not for me. I don't want to be here. So what if we're seeing in the year 2000? I don't know what the fuss is all about. This is overrated, I'm thinking to myself. Sitting there nursing a light beer, not so much as a single party atom pulsing in my body, I'm withdrawn, not good company. Friends drift by and engage me in conversation but my responses are minimal, barely courteous. This is hard work. My gaze keeps drifting to my watch, observing the dragging of time as the hands climb unhurriedly towards midnight. Come on! Let's get this over with. I don't want to be here.

Louise and I say our goodnights, shut the car doors, buckle ourselves in and drive home to a January that will be every bit as uninspiring as the February to follow. The manic elevator has gone beyond the top of the climb. Now comes the black fall into depression. The harness ties have snapped and I'm plunging into the abyss.

———

In the Olympic year, the football season kicks off early; but my return to the sideline and its intimate proximity to the heat of the sporting battle does nothing to raise my spirits or fire the old adrenalin. Instead, while staying with friends Tracey Holmes and Brodie Carr on Sydney rugby league weekends, I am less than the perfect house guest. After breakfasting with them on a Sunday morning at Manly Corso, I have to excuse myself and head back to their unit to sleep. Such is the state of my exhaustion. The light at the end of this tunnel should be the prospect of my selection on the ABC's Olympics team. During the drives to arrive on time at a Sydney rugby league ground or strapped into my seat on an interstate flight, I often consider the possibility of working on the Games. But as my thoughts ramble down that long corridor, there is no light at the end, only an endless gauntlet of sheer hard work. Somewhere amid these ruminations, the notion takes shape: 'Hey, I'm not going to be that shattered if I don't make it to the Olympics.'

My application to work on the ABC's News team had been lodged and rejected on the basis that I wasn't news trained. The last opportunity rests with securing a place as a sports reporter but I haven't submitted a formal application for that role. To tell the truth, I have quit lobbying. I don't care. The biggest gig on the planet is right here on the doorstep and I no longer give a flying fig whether I make it there or not.

Mid-March: 'I think I'm mildly depressed,' I hear myself telling Louise for the first time.

By now, my wife has had enough of my moping around. She considers this for a moment and says: 'I don't think you are; but if you are, do something about it, will you?'

No matter how calmly that advice has been expressed, it is pregnant with a precious item of loving wisdom. I ignore it. After all, I'm an Australian man. We catch and kill our own demons.

The moment comes and goes and life's muddled march carries us on into April. Once easy, work has become harder, as if the landscape has been tilted and I'm pushing my load up an ever-steepening hill. Where has my energy gone? Wherever; my sharp focus has gone with it! It is difficult to concentrate and I am easily distracted. Thoughts are jumbled. Maybe a return to the playing field, where everything was once so simple, will clear the fog. I'm standing in a corner of Alder Park, home of budding soccer champions for almost a hundred years. Around me cavort Josh and his mates from the New Lambton South under-9s, mucking about like boys do while bending one expectant ear for the coach to bring them to order. An invigorating autumn breeze cuts across the park, furling the last of the summer grass and catching the boys' calls as they chase the ball. In my role as coach, I see and hear it all but the core of my being remains oblivious to the ageless beauty of the moment. Neither the joy of children's voices nor the vigour of an autumn wind can move the cloud.

May. Who is this man who snaps at his children like

that? It is not as if they have suddenly turned into gremlins. They're good kids, always have been. But here I am biting their heads off at the slightest fault. A spilt drink is met with the sort of fury a normal bloke might display if his ankle-biters had set fire to the garage. The look in their eyes is one of hurt. It says, 'Hey, Dad, we haven't done anything wrong.' This impulse to agitation and aggression leaps out of the dark at the slightest pretext. If it is not targeting the kids, then it is launching itself at Louise. Soft targets all. The verbal eruption never fits the crime.

Maybe I'm on the brink. On arriving home of an afternoon, when Louise is at work, my fatherly duty is to make the kids a snack, help them with their homework, supervise their play, prepare dinner, give them a bath and pop them between the sheets with a bedtime story. In households all over Australia, thousands of dads are performing the same ritual. Yet, I'm struggling. Instead of sweeping the little ones into my arms, I throw myself on the floor, exhausted. Locked up in school all day, the kids are full of beans, pleased to see me. 'Out!' I bark, banishing them to the yard. I just want some peace.

At that point, *right there*, the sirens should have been screaming, lights flashing, bells ringing. A neon sign should have lit up the night sky with the message: 'CRAIG HAMILTON, YOU'VE GOT PROBLEMS! DO SOMETHING ABOUT IT!'

Hey, I *am* doing something about it. They've taken blood samples to see if I'm suffering from chronic fatigue, an iron deficiency or some other disorder. I'm having a weekly massage to relax me. I'm off the booze and drinking herbal tea. Here's a yoga membership receipt in my wallet and I've already been to a few sessions. Take a look at my bedside reading – it's all about relaxation techniques. The diet is all quality, I'm getting plenty of exercise . . .

But it's not working.

The sleep patterns are more erratic. The agitation and aggression are still prevalent. And, of late, I can feel this awful fist of anxiety in the centre of my abdomen every waking day.

———

Mid year: 'Good morning, 1233 ABC Newcastle, you're with Craig Hamilton.' The cheery Saturday greeting is all an act. Once the introductions are out of the way I start selecting the longest playing tracks on the discs at hand. 'Baker Street' by Gerry Rafferty runs six minutes or so; 'Oh No, Not You Again' by Australian Crawl is a solid five minutes. They're played back-to-back as I curl up in a foetal position on the studio floor, immobilised by despair.

Every fibre of my being tells me I'm in a bad way, but I'm still trying to work. The task of getting out of bed, showering, dressing and making my way to work is as daunting and tiring as building the pyramids – one foot after the other, an eternal stone tethered to my soul. Miraculously, the front holds. The voice coming through the microphone and over the airwaves to radios in workplaces, vehicles and homes sounds as cheerful as ever. Nobody would guess; not by listening.

In terms of work ethic and responsibility, I'll always be

eternally grateful to the example of my parents. Their lives have been monuments to fortitude. They never ducked it, not for a second. Hereditary or learned, that grit and determination had delivered the best life had to offer. Likewise in sport; reward usually lay beyond the pain barrier. To endure was to win. Out of such struggles is character built. These values are reference points and they are hard won. The irony with this battle was that they were principles I would have to abandon in order to survive. Instead of persisting on my own, I would have to give myself over – to seek help.

———

'I think I'm depressed.'

'Why do you think you're depressed?' asks our family doctor.

Good question. 'Because I'm not sleeping very well; I have negative thoughts all the time; I'm absolutely exhausted; I've lost weight; I'm not eating properly; I'm cranky with my kids all the time; and I have no sex drive whatsoever. All of those things are not the bloke that I know. I read in a book that if you have three of those symptoms, there is every chance you are suffering from depression. I have all of those symptoms.'

'You have diagnosed yourself correctly,' our GP says. 'You are clinically depressed.'

This is a big kick in the guts. I had desperately wanted him to disprove my theory. Instead, he has just told me what I had already expected; but it is still a tough message to cop.

'What are we going to do about it?' probes the doctor, and before I can offer an answer to his rhetorical question he continues, 'We're going to prescribe antidepressant medication.'

That's not what I want to hear. 'I don't think so,' I begin. 'Um, blokes don't take antidepressants and –'

He has seen and heard it all before. 'Look,' he interjects, 'depression is common; it's very treatable and this is very good medication.'

Reluctantly, I bow to his wisdom and, script in hand, present myself at the local pharmacy to collect a course of Lovan (fluoxetine hydrochloride), a Prozac equivalent, wondering if I'll bump into anyone I know and they'll ask what the hell is up with me. How would I explain? Other than Louise and our GP, I haven't told anybody. You don't tell anybody. You just battle on. Yet, perhaps having that script filled, reading the instructions, popping the first capsule from the blister pack, have caused me to cross a bridge. Have I now passed the point of denial? If so, I should tell my parents.

I'm on my way to my home town for what should be a magical day – an annual golfing catch-up between four Singleton blokes – Greg Moore, Peter Dunn, Barry Smith and me. The plan is to assemble at Singleton and then drive down the valley to the Lower Hunter vineyards and play the magnificent Cypress Lakes course. By any reckoning, this should be a fabulous reunion. We do this every year – sledge the daylights out of each other from the first to the 18th hole, enjoy a few beers, reminisce, catch up on news and share plenty of laughs. When the round is finished, our wives will join us at a restaurant among the vines for dinner.

I'd be looking forward to this with absolute relish but for the fact I'm feeling as flat as week-old roadkill. I don't want to go. My thoughts aren't of golf and the vineyards. Instead, I'm thinking about my parents. I have left home early with the plan to swing by the family farm and tell my folks that life for their eldest child isn't exactly a stroll in the park. This is not easy. As a parent I sense the need that all parents have for the outcomes to be favourable for their children. Whether we want it that way or not, we will always see the success or failures of our children as a measure of ourselves. What child, particularly a 37-year-old, wants to lay these troubles at his parents' door at a time in their lives when they merit the balmy solace of their own Indian summer? Perhaps what eludes me the most is the means to tell my mum – the retired nurse – and my dad – the bloke who wouldn't let a broken pelvis knock him off his feet – that their son may look okay, but he is actually doing it tough. I feel like the shell-shocked veteran returning home, envying his mates with their crutches and bandages. A shattered limb would need no explanation.

I walk in the front door and collapse on the lounge. 'Listen, I need to talk to you both.'

Their body language tells me they know it is something serious.

'I'm having a really tough time at the moment,' I start. 'I'm depressed. In fact, I've been diagnosed with clinical depression and, as of today, I'm on antidepressants. I just hope things will turn around but it's been getting worse and worse . . . and I just need you to know.'

Here are two people who have had their own share of life's battles, standing in their front room hearing this from their eldest child and father of three of their grandchildren. How will they react?

There is no deliberation. Mum and Dad are immediately supportive, understanding. They haven't run the other way or gone into denial. They know this is serious. Now there are five people who know.

————

Golf goes off without a hitch. My façade is up and the day passes smoothly until we get to dinner, where I realise I am struggling to keep up appearances. The table talk is about friends and acquaintances from our shared Singleton days. One of the boys is relating an account so tragically typical of country towns of late. It's about a guy he knew who has just taken his own life, leaving a wife and three kids.

'What a selfish bastard,' remarks one of the boys.

The comment hits me like a club. I find myself saying, 'Gee, he must have been doing it tough.'

Mercifully, the conversation changes tack and we move into safer waters. I'm not ready to share the story with my mates.

Day two of the antidepressants: I'm starting to wonder if these tablets work.

Day three: I'm feeling worse. They obviously don't work, I'm thinking.

Day nine: things are worse. I'm having suicidal thoughts.

Down the track I would learn that I should have been on the medication months before but pride, stupidity, ego or whatever had barred me from seeking help. We're used to antibiotics going to work right away. It would take time for the medication to address the chemical imbalance in my brain. Now, I'm learning that I still have a way to go before I'll bottom out.

As for my close friends, I realise they need to know. Sometime during the preceding week, I've picked up the phone, dialled the usual suspects and imparted the news. I'm struggling, I need some space. The response is a mixture of surprise and concern. But all are one hundred percent supportive. For the moment, all the space I need is about the size of a grown man curled into a foetal position. This prenatal posture hints at helplessness, coiled up in bed, unable to move. My body appears inert but my mind is racing like a caged squirrel, frantically turning over ideas, looking for a way out of this pit.

It's four in the morning. I'm wide awake. My shoulders are on fire with the intensity of a sadist torturing me with a blowtorch. I stumble out of bed and into the bathroom, shed my clothes and stand under the cold shower to quell the blistering pain across my upper back. The agony is inexorable and I frantically search my mind for another form of relief. That's it! If I can make my exhaustion more potent than the pain, then perhaps I will be able to sleep. Blearily, I pull on my joggers, telling myself that exercise is the answer. This will help.

A couple of hundred metres from home, I'm absolutely shattered, unable to continue another step. Groggy from pain, torment and sleep deprivation, tears rolling down my cheeks, I struggle to get my bearings. My pitiful journey has halted outside a building larger than the flanking houses. Confused, I look up at its imposing façade and slowly recognise the familiar outline of St Therese's Church. I stumble up the front steps and try to open the doors. They are locked. *Why would they lock a bloody church?* I'm yelling to myself.

I retreat back down the steps and look up, my gaze following the vaulted arch to the crowning cross. I am in intense physical and emotional pain, and at the absolute end of my rope. Just when there is nothing left to give, a voice emanates from the pit of my tortured soul. Now, I've delivered radio reports from steamy dressing rooms and sodden sidelines under all sorts of pressures, but this message is something else again. It's a wonder the Great Producer up there doesn't send it back for reworking: 'God,' I hear myself saying, 'I've never really known if you're there or not; but if you are there, now is the time to do something. Act now, please God, because I have nothing left.'

7

SIDELINED

The football season is three-parts gone but I'm not working. If I were in the right frame of mind, Peter Wilkins' comment would crease me with laughter. On hearing the news that I need time off because I am depressed, Wilko says: 'You take a pill for that, don't you?'

'I'm already on the pills,' is my wry response.

The ABC has granted me sick-leave on receipt of a certificate from my doctor. At my request he has filled in the 'nature of illness' line with the word 'virus'. Two more certificates and two more weeks follow before I instruct our GP to write the real reason for my absence. With 'depression' on the form, I have outed myself, if only to the ABC station manager. Among my colleagues, there is not so much as a single raised eyebrow. Most of them remain unaware of the true nature of my condition. In another time and place the advice might be: 'Shout yourself six beers and get over it' or, more bluntly: 'Wake up to yourself!'

At home, where I wallow in a cavern of gloom, the spectre of suicide darts in and out of my thinking. I don't want to die; but please give me a ticket out of this agony. Louise, dressed for work, appears by our bedside where her unwell and unhappy husband lies curled. She knows I'm depressed but, at this stage, has no understanding of the unfathomable depth of my desperation and misery. I'm hoping I won't have to tell her; I'm hoping the antidepressants will kick in and the dark clouds will part. Twenty-four hours after my early-morning meltdown outside of St Therese's, the tragic news has done the rounds of our neighbourhood: a troubled young man known to us has taken his own life. My wife looks down at me and says: 'Thank God you're not that bad.'

I don't reply.

She nudges my leg. 'Thank God you've never thought like that.'

No reply.

'Craig, look at me! You've never had those kinds of thoughts, have you?'

Turning to face my wife, I blurt it out: those thoughts have crossed my mind.

She folds before my eyes; sits down on the bed and weeps inconsolably. Somewhere in the loving structure we have built together – home, family, partnership – a wall has blown down and the wind and the rain come streaming through on everything she cherishes.

Louise must have arrived at work in a terrible state. One of her colleagues, thankfully, has sent her straight back home to keep an eye on her suicidal husband.

When all the crying is done we sit together as life partners and have the long-deferred tête-à-tête. This time, I leave nothing to chance. Nothing is left unsaid. If there is an end to the decline, this is it – rock bottom. This day saved my life.

———

The antidepressants are working. Their effect is tangible. As if a gentle draught is clearing condensation from a windowpane, the vista is slowly taking shape again. But I am impatient and needing assurance. Every day I ask Louise if she notices my improvement. It is totally self-indulgent and must be testing her patience, but I need to believe. There is no doubt, my condition is improving.

Four weeks sick-leave have expired and I feel ready to return to my sideline-eye role with the ABC's rugby league coverage. In response to calls from listeners, Wilko has explained that I was 'a bit crook' but promised I'd be back. And I am back – tentative and nervous, but back. It's a West Tigers home game at Campbelltown and I have the feeling that the training wheels are on and it takes all of my focus to keep the wobbles under control. But I get through.

Ostensibly, life has returned to a sort of normal. With

the Lovan leaching deep into the runnels and funnels of my mind, working its alchemy as a selective serotonin reuptake inhibitor, the depression slowly but surely retreats. I return to work, convinced a nasty episode in my life journey has been encountered and conquered.

At this point I feel vindicated about ignoring a piece of advice imparted by my doctor. On a number of occasions throughout 2000, he had wanted to refer me to a psychiatrist. At first I had resisted the initiative and, as the antidepressants made me feel better, I became convinced I was in need of no such help.

I'm back in the weekly workflow at ABC Newcastle. The momentum of the football season carries me forward to the play-offs and, when the Brisbane Broncos defeat the Sydney City Roosters at Olympic Stadium, I am right there in the thick of it all doing my job. You should not mix alcohol with antidepressants but that night I see off the season with a few drinks, telling myself that, after all I have been through, I am entitled to a bit of latitude.

When you stand too close to a picture, you can see only a bit of it – not the whole. The farther back you walk, the clearer the overall view. From where I was standing, I could see a deep depression out of which I had just crawled. I thought my melancholy was the entire story. Later, when compelled to take an even longer view, I would see two towering summits of mania either side of the depression. This would be my first glimpse of the terrible sweep of bipolar disorder. But for now, I was totally convinced my ailment was depression and I had fought the beast and emerged battered but alive. The trap for medical practitioners is that patients do not present for treatment when they are riding the heights of the mania; they usually do not seek help until the depression becomes unbearable. This syndrome often results in an early misdiagnosis, leaving the mania side of the equation to kick-start the process all over again.

———

Late August 2000: Alan Marks is in an ebullient mood. The guided tour of the International Broadcasting Centre in Sydney is reserved for the privileged few.

'The Americans will be there, the BBC there, the Japanese have booked this area, the Seven Network is over there and we'll be right here,' says the ABC Sport boss, coming to a halt in the media nerve-centre of the Games of the XXVII Olympiad. 'And, Craig, this is where you'll be based, working with a producer and calling action straight off the tube, telling us what's happening from any of the venues.'

More than a decade in the planning, seven years in the making, the event has stretched our sense of anticipation beyond all limits. We're talking about ten thousand athletes, 200 participating countries and a worldwide audience of 3.5 billion! Now it is almost upon us and here I am on a personal introductory tour of my workplace for the greatest month in Australian sports history.

Right across the nation, and perhaps the entire world, you can sense the excitement building. Deep inside my psyche another series of small reactors comes on line, firing up the pulse, lifting the tempo of my thought processes. My mood is good, strong, getting stronger. In two weeks time I'll be here. *Bring it on!* My energy is back, the old Craig has returned. I'm buzzing like a boy in a lolly shop. Sleep? Four hours a night is more than enough as I power through my workload preparing myself for the big gig.

ABC presenter and Newcastle colleague Madeleine Randall has an idea for her New South Wales-wide program on the Sunday before the Games. She quietly approaches me midweek with her proposal for an on-air discussion on the big subject of depression. Somewhere in the back of my mind I had wanted to use my experience with depression to help others, but I figured it would be way down the track. Madeleine has sown a seed. Would I be happy to join her and psychologist William Findlay on air to talk about the taboo subject? I'm feeling strong, confident, even a bit gung-ho. My inclusion on the Olympic team is proof enough that I have beaten the demons. I agree to go public about my predicament on air that Sunday.

———

Sunday, 10 September, 10 am: I am ready to spill my guts live on air. After the intros, Madeleine brings me in with the comment: 'Craig, you've had a tough time of late.'

I'd been wondering just how to get into this subject and have prepared a strategy. 'Madeleine,' I begin, 'before we get into that I want to tell you about a mate of mine. He's a great bloke, a real knockabout guy. I know him very well – better than anybody actually. I saw him ten weeks ago at a Newcastle Knights game. He was sitting in his usual position and I said, "G'day, how are you going?" and he said, "Great." He was fine, he looked good to me. A little while later I saw him at a Knights corporate lunch and I asked him how he was going and he said, "As good as gold." Now, this bloke is a really good mate. He's got a great wife and great kids. He has great friends, the best job in the world, no money worries whatsoever. I saw him again five weeks ago and he said he was "good".

'I just want you to know that five weeks ago he was actually thinking about taking his own life. He was thinking about suicide as an option because he was that low with depressive illness. When people asked him how he was going, he replied, "I'm going good, mate," because that's what you do in Australia – even if you are going shithouse. And he was going shithouse. He was suicidal. I happen to know this all for a fact because that bloke was me . . .'

The switchboard is lighting up with callers. We take calls from Mudgee, Wee Waa and right around the state. People are phoning to tell us about bush suicides. Farmers ring to talk about depression, broken families and loved ones taking their own lives after suffering in silence. The calls keep coming. We have hit an exposed nerve.

'No-one is talking about it,' I say. 'And you know why? It is not sexy, not fashionable, it is stigmatised. Many people won't want to hear this, in fact there must be friends of mine out there who have no idea what I've been through.

But it is too important not to speak out about it, because people are suffering.'

We pause for a promo and William taps me on the shoulder to say: 'This is powerful stuff. You're advancing the cause here. You've thrown more light on this subject in the past half-hour than we've achieved in the last twenty years.'

For two hours we connect with families, so many of whom have lost loved ones – particularly dads and sons – to suicide. I issue a warning to everyone listening not to ignore the signs. I feel good. It is therapeutic.

With the show over, I'm heading home where we are expecting our close friends from Singleton, Barry and Donna Smith and their children, to join us for lunch. They have tuned in to the program on the drive down. They are late. Perhaps they've taken time to compose themselves. It can't have been easy listening for my friends and family. No doubt it was very hard for Barry and Donna to come to lunch that day. It was their first real indication I had been through the mincer.

Much later, Barry would tell me that he sensed things were not quite right that Sunday. 'Over the top' would be the expression he used to describe my demeanour. After that lunch, he and I found a private moment together and I told him where I had been. He knew things weren't okay. By the time we had finished talking, he had tears in his eyes. I was thinking they must have been tears of joy for my recovery. Now, I understand he was thinking: 'This is not the guy I grew up with, played cricket and footy with, attended each other's weddings. What has happened to that bloke?'

Louise, too, suspected that something wasn't quite right. She knew I had hardly slept for the previous four nights. I had been up and down, making notes, sifting through files, and going over my Olympic preparations.

Me? There is a smile on my face; I am feeling on top of the world.

The mania is building.

———

When I cast my thoughts back to that time, I have a vision, almost cartoon-like in its nature. It is one of those classic situations in which our likeable fool thinks that he is standing safely on terra firma. In fact, he has his feet planted on something so huge and vast that he cannot see where it starts or finishes so he mistakes it for solid ground. It's a bit like Daffy Duck finding himself on dry land in the middle of the swamp only to realise that the solid ground under his feet has started moving and, rather than bedrock, it is actually the grand-daddy of all crocodiles. This little black duck's mental picture has my feet firmly planted on a raft floating in what I perceive as sheltered waters. I have no way of knowing that far beneath me, a hidden hand is lifting the ocean floor, creating a truly overwhelming energy force as it multiplies in power with each pulsing of its rise. Each day, I unknowingly draw vigour from its vast reserves, my mood escalating with the pressure building indiscernibly under my feet. Anonymously, it gathers itself, swelling with the latent strength of a thousand Krakatoas. Meanwhile, our likeable fool cavorts on his raft, each day more manic than the last. The tsunami is on its way.

———

Monday, 5 am: I'm wide awake looking out the window and can see a star. It's bigger and brighter than any other in the sky. *That's a sign.* Out of bed after just three hours sleep. There's much to be done. This is an important time in my career. I'm off to the Games tomorrow! Who, me? *Yes, you Craig Hamilton. Can't you see how this was meant to happen?*

The human brain is the most amazing of organs. It can conceive of anything. But when its chemistry goes wrong, the mind is capable of constructing an alternative universe. The smallest particle of fallacy can grow, exponentially, into an entire panorama of delusion of the grandest proportions. My in-laws, Pat and Sue Kelly, are here with Louise and we're looking through my clippings, awards and certificates. Stories about miraculous sporting achievements and events. *Look at your life. Look at the journey you have taken. Think about your destiny. Didn't you see the star yesterday morning? Yes, yes, the Olympics are important, but there's something far bigger at play here and you have a role in it. A big role. Maybe the biggest role of all. This was all meant to happen for a reason. You and the Olympics – an incredible conjunction. Can't you see, Craig, how destiny is playing out? Can't you see who you are and what your real purpose is going to be? Admit it Craig, you know who you are.*

I'm, I'm . . .

Yes, just admit it to yourself.

I'm Jesus Christ!

In my head is a finely tuned speech ready for delivery at the closing ceremony of the Olympics. The message is: put down your weapons. To the rich nations: feed the hungry, cross starvation off the list as a killer of human beings. Embrace one another as fellow humans – not black, white, rich or poor. Love one another. Rid the world of weapons which have the capacity to destroy the planet. All supporters of terrorism will be put on notice by an enlightened world demanding peace. I dare not commit the speech to paper for fear that it will be discovered by evil forces. Christ has returned and their positions of strength from where they have peddled death, destruction and unhappiness will be exposed by a greater force for good – Jesus Christ Himself.

Tuesday afternoon: There's a train to catch. Bag in the boot, kids buckled in the back, Louise by my side, we're heading for Broadmeadow railway station. I'm on a mission.

8

AFTER THE DELUGE

A few of our neighbours had encountered me on that fateful Tuesday morning and all would say that they had noticed nothing out of the ordinary about my mood or conduct. Louise would later relate that arriving back at the railway station to see her husband in a psychotic state explained everything. Considering where I had been with the depression, it would have been difficult for anyone to have picked what was happening to me in the days leading up to the breakdown at Broadmeadow. In a strange way, as horrific as it was, there must have been a tiny sense of release for Louise because at least it explained the events of the previous week.

After my discharge from James Fletcher Hospital and a

month of home rest, I was kicking my heels in absolute boredom, desperate to return to work. That wasn't going to happen until I had been cleared by an independent psychiatric report. No problem. I was one hundred percent certain it would be a mere formality. Hey, I was feeling fine! The medication had definitely stabilised me. I had worked my way through the disappointment of having missed the Olympics. It was a period of crossing off the days on the calendar until my appointment.

Dr Puru Sager is a Maitland-based psychiatrist and a member of a panel appointed to deal with government employees. He has rooms in Newcastle, which is where I confidently presented myself for assessment. After the introductions, Dr Sager came to the point: he was aware that in my time at James Fletcher I had divulged my belief that I was Jesus Christ and had a grand plan for the Olympics. Did I still hold to that conviction?

'Clearly, I wasn't well,' I responded. 'In fact, I was very unwell. I'm very mortal like everybody else. I'm not Jesus; I'm just a sports broadcaster who has been off work for five weeks and would dearly love to return. I'm bored.'

He was very understanding and compassionate. After forty minutes or so, Dr Sager said: 'Okay, that's about it. We'll let you know the results.'

It was October, the height of spring, when I stepped back out on to the pavement for what could have been a new beginning. But my impression was that the interview had not gone as well as it might have. Judging by his body language, Dr Sager had appeared anything but convinced.

At home, I sat close to the phone. It didn't ring. Two days passed; still no call. Three days. On the fourth day, impatience got the better of me so I dialled the ABC and spoke to one of my superiors. 'Listen,' I began, 'I've been to see the psychiatrist for my assessment and haven't heard a thing.'

There was a brief silence at the other end. Then, 'Um, look, ah . . . Dr Sager says you're not ready to return to work yet. You need to go and see him again down the track. But, for now, he hasn't passed you fit to return.'

This was a real kick in the guts. 'The guy is wrong,' I spluttered. 'He's . . . he's just got it wrong.'

In Dr Sager's opinion my mood was still elevated. Sure, the medication had brought it down considerably but it had a fair way to go. From his observation, I was still talking incessantly and was still wired. What sort of judge was I? Dr Sager's assessment was absolutely accurate. There is no doubt that had he rubber-stamped me for a return to work at that time, I would have been very vulnerable. As a professional, his assessment was spot on.

Another four weeks would go by before my second visit to Dr Sager. The monotony was broken by a series of visits to psychologist William Findlay. It had been quite a journey since we had joined Madeleine Randall for that Sunday morning program on depression but our three sessions together kicked off on a positive note and, in my view, I made great progress. We looked at the whole picture: depression, medication, my personality type, work structure, family relationships. My diary notation read: 'I'm greatly heartened by this cognitive therapy process as it encourages me to examine the way these elements inter-relate, to recognise what has gone awry in my life and to move on'.

One month after my discharge from hospital, we cele-brated the 'Kiss a Disastrous 2000 Goodbye Weekend'. It was the first chance since the Broadmeadow crash that Louise and I had had to spend quality time alone together. Leaving the kids with Louise's mum and dad we headed for the Eaglereach bush retreat near Vacy in the Hunter Valley. We read, relaxed, had a spa, slept, ate and stepped out on the four-kilometre, two-way bushwalk to breakfast each morning. We also did something we had never done before: met across the table for a game of pool. I'm supposed to be the athlete in the family but this contest went right down to a black-ball game. Louise duly potted the black and then, delirious with laughter, denied me the opportunity of a rematch, telling me she would never play me at pool again so that her undefeated record would remain intact. She hadn't laughed so much in a long time.

Reunited with the kids after that weekend, I noted that Josh was on edge. Having us out of sight for a couple of days obviously evoked the uncertainty of the time sur-rounding my hospitalisation. Choosing my moment I took him aside and quietly reassured him that we were together as a family and everything would be all right.

My diary entries of the time repeatedly refer to how exhausted I felt and note Louise's comments on how tired I looked. As keen as I was about getting back to work, I had to admit that the enforced break was bound to do me some good. As the march of time put space between us and the events of 12 September, my fixation with that day and the resultant hospitalisation was starting to diminish. There was still a determination to get to the bottom of it all, but it was no longer consuming my every waking thought. In my head I had replayed the process of depression, breakdown, mania, psychosis, delusion and then back to a semblance of normality. Yet, I continued to question the entire process. One thing I know is that I'll never again take the antidepressant Lovan. My memory of ten days on the medication culminating in anxiety and suicidal thoughts is too painful. I have since learned that antidepressants for sufferers of bipolar type I should be used strictly under psychiatric care and in conjunction with mood stabilisers.

Louise and I looked for distractions that harked back to happier times. As a young courting couple our idea of a great night out had been to catch a headline act performing live at a local pub or club. So, when Glenn Shorrock came to town in October, we snagged a couple of tickets and went along for a night of pure nostalgia and escapism. We both needed it.

In the period following my discharge from hospital, my professional care and rehabilitation was placed in the hands of a number of practitioners. My status as an outpatient under the auspices of the Mental Health Unit required me to attend a series of appointments with psychiatrist Dr Ivan Safranco. As mentioned earlier, the assessment of my fitness to return to work fell to Dr Puru Sager. To further help me make sense of my predicament, I continued my consultations with William Findlay. Additionally, I returned to see my family GP, who referred my ongoing psychiatric care to Dr Alan Weiss. Since February 2001, Dr Weiss has been my sole professional consultant and I see him on a regular basis.

———

Newcastle and the Lower Hunter form a community of almost half a million people, but in many ways the area retains the closeness of a much smaller place. The degrees of separation are 0.6 rather than six. That closeness is tighter still if people feel they know you via your job as a media personality. However, there is enough of the old world left in Newcastle for people to still look out for each other. On a slow news day the dramatic tale of a local ABC broadcaster running amok and being carted off Broadmeadow railway station by the constabulary might have made for a colourful yarn in the local paper or on the evening news bulletin. Editors and journalists around town had all heard about my breakdown but they did our family and friends a mercy by not running the yarn. It's the sort of kindness you don't quickly forget.

Out on the street it was a bit different. Friends and associates had heard about my plight and were interested in my welfare. With Laura at pre-school, we were out having lunch when we ran into Elaine, the mother of my ABC colleague Katja Akik (Baidoo), plus Christine Tyler, Joshua's speech pathologist and wife of Mike Tyler, deputy chairman of the Newcastle Knights. They both asked how I was feeling and I found that the more I spoke with them about it, the better I felt. It was definitely cathartic.

The sessions with William Findlay were also broadening my self-awareness as we discussed the relationship between the experiences of childhood and adolescent trauma, the internalising of grief and the link between them and a resultant breakdown. On my own part, I was determined to eat and exercise well. With time on my hands I found myself swimming laps at nearby Lambton pool. Despite the lingering feelings of tiredness the exercise was a welcome release.

One duty I had to perform was to reassure Madeleine Randall that she had nothing to do with my breakdown. This notion would be almost funny but for the fact that Madeleine believed her idea of inviting me on to talk about depression had somehow triggered the crazy events at Broadmeadow. She was genuinely devastated at the news of my hospitalisation and had phoned Louise to say that she felt terrible and was blaming herself for what had happened. Madeleine is a compassionate, caring soul and it would take a bit to convince her that, despite her worst fears, she had nothing whatsoever to do with my mishap.

A chance to pop my head back in the office presented itself with the retirement of our long-time gardening expert and legendary nurseryman Bill Whalan. Bill had been a fixture on my Saturday morning show so I dropped by for his farewell and said a few words. Over coffee and cake, I fell into a one-on-one chat with broadcaster and workmate Garth Russell. To this point, nobody outside of Louise, Chris Williams and Kathy Stewart, and the mental health professionals, had been given a true insight into the seriousness of my breakdown on the railway station. Garth listened in incredulous silence as I gave him a blow-by-blow account of my Jesus delusion, the events at the station and my hospitalisation. Being so forthcoming when the wound was still so raw was a big leap for me. On the drive home, I wondered whether I had overstepped the mark by exposing so much.

In the ensuing weeks, the boredom associated with my time off work would be relieved by visits from the much put-upon Chris Williams and Kathy Stewart. If apologies were needed then mine should have been profuse to the man I had so violently abused on Broadmeadow station. But as we enjoyed lunch and reflected on a day none of us will soon forget, Chris made light of my contrition and reiterated how happy he was to see me on the mend.

A couple of our dearest friends from Singleton, Bruce and Simone Robinson and their kids, also called in for lunch, affirming again the strength to be drawn from those who care most about our welfare. I also found time for tea and a chat with Paul 'The Chief' Harragon, the inspirational captain who had led the Knights to a miraculous 1997 grand final victory and had moved on to an impressive media career and a position as a high-profile advocate for numerous charitable causes. Paul and I had spoken at length before my session on the Madeleine Randall show and I valued his support and counsel. There was a hint of irony here, too, relating back to the movie *One Flew Over the Cuckoo's Nest*. Paul's nickname 'The Chief' stemmed from his teenage years when his large proportions and long straight hair inspired his mates to name him after the big Native American in the movie. The Chief and Randall McMurphy (me) were back together comparing notes.

Other visitors included my workmates: station manager Mike McCluskey, program director Linda Bracken, announcer Paul Turton and producer Lucia Hill all dropped by for coffee and a chat. Another caller was Warren Ryan. My partner on the ABC's rugby league team and former coaching great had driven from Sydney to check on my progress. Compared with Warren, I had been a relative rugby league ignoramus but one who was willing to learn. During our working time together he had patiently imparted so much of his golden wisdom and insight on the game. No football journalist could have had a finer tutor. It was great to see him and my other colleagues. I didn't sense any discomfort or distance. Rather, their presence reaffirmed my desire to rejoin the team at work. Once again, I was confident the second visit to Dr Sager would formalise the matter.

The assessment flowed smoothly with me reiterating how well I felt and how much I longed to return to the job. Dr Sager worked his way through a list of questions. From my side of the desk, it had all gone fine. So, imagine my disbelief and disappointment on learning I had been knocked back again with the doctor's recommendation that I still required a further two to three months off work. My response at the time was mild outrage. This couldn't be right. I wrote in my diary:

In my humble opinion, the bloke is just plain wrong. I've experienced depression and I know that I am certainly no longer depressed. I have experienced one episode of mania and am certain I am neither manic nor depressed. What sort of guarantees does Sager require before recommending my return to work? Would it not be in my best interests to return to the workplace sooner rather than later and be monitored by colleagues, friends and family rather than be left sitting at home?

But, yet again, as I reassess that time from a greater distance, I recognise just how correct the evaluation was.

My frustration was on a slow simmer. It had been seven weeks since the Broadmeadow breakdown and I still hadn't returned to work. What do you do when you don't believe a practitioner? Get a second opinion, of course. I phoned Mike McCluskey to vent my frustration. 'Dr Sager won't let me return to work,' I said. 'I'm ready. In fact, I believe I was ready five weeks ago. Get me someone else. Find me another psychiatrist.'

Mike calmly referred me to Kath O'Brien, the ABC's Head of Human Resources. She explained that there was a panel of five, of which Dr Sager was one.

'Well, let's go to another one,' I suggested. 'I want a second opinion.'

Dr Graham Vickery's rooms are in Darby Street, Cooks Hill – a Newcastle street famous for its quality coffee. But on 11 November – Remembrance Day – I eschewed the alluring aroma of coffee beans, steering clear of caffeine or anything else that might have unnecessarily elevated my mood as I kept my appointment with the psychiatrist. He opened a folder containing all my case notes and reports. Once again, the interview ran for about forty minutes, at the end of which he pushed back his chair and uttered the words I'd been longing to hear: 'You're okay, you can go back to work.'

9

DENIAL

Getting back on the bike wasn't necessarily easy. After almost two months off work I was bound to feel a bit out of touch. Moreover, the circumstances of my absence dictated my mood: trepidation and a little tentative. But when you've been through the wringer and come out the other side, it's imperative you count the blessings as they fall your way. It was my good fortune to be returning to a wonderful workplace peopled by great characters. They all knew what I had been through but nobody wrapped me in cotton-wool or fussed. Rather, there was a feeling of warm support backed by the few heartfelt words I needed to hear: 'Great to see you back, Craig.' The tone was set at the first staff meeting of the week when I was officially welcomed back and given a spontaneous round of applause. It said it all.

On a personal level, I was seeking ways to bring balance to my life. My diary from the time reads: 'Goals – to continue to practise yoga, spend time with Louise and the kids, don't worry about things beyond my control, eat, sleep and exercise well, read more books on eastern philosophy.'

Dr Ivan Safranco was a big fan of the ABC and said how much he'd missed my Saturday morning show while I'd been off work. His easy professional manner was very reassuring. In his company I certainly didn't feel like a stigmatised mental patient, but more like an average worker who had needed time off as the result of a conventional health setback. By this stage I was off all my post-breakdown medication with the exception of Epilim. We were now in the process of seeing that the reintroduction to meaningful employment went smoothly. Just when I was feeling quite relaxed, he threw me a curve ball.

'We've had a look at your admission to hospital, your history through 2000, depression, the time on the antidepressants, the mania and the psychosis,' said the psychiatrist, 'and it all adds up to bipolar disorder.'

Even though 'displaying symptom of bipolar disorder' had been mentioned at James Fletcher, this time there was no blurring of the edges: this was a definite, stark diagnosis by an eminent psychiatrist – a professional with half an alphabet of letters after his name and a shiny brass plaque on his front door. Did I accept this assessment? No. By now, I had a pretty good track record for disagreeing with the experts.

'Nope, no way.' I knew that bipolar disorder was just another name for manic depression. I'd heard the term used to describe problems encountered by Johnny 'The Wild One' O'Keefe, Spike Milligan, Winston Churchill, Ted Turner, Jim Carrey, Brian Wilson, Buzz Aldrin, Marilyn Monroe and a bunch of other high-profile people who had wrestled with these demons all their lives. No, that wasn't me. I was just a bloke who had experienced a momentary setback and was in the process of returning his life to normal. Stepping out of Dr Safranco's office, I was in a very introspective mood. A small part of me conceded that the diagnosis could be right. But that germ of a thought was drowned by the overriding conviction that the psychiatrist had to be wrong. Bipolar disorder? No, that's not me. I'm not that guy.

I was feeling good. My thinking was: 'Let's not categorise this. My setback is not something that needs to be given a name. Don't stick that label on me. I don't need the stigma of being tagged with a mental disorder. I'm not carrying that cross. It was just something that happened. Let's move on.'

It's amazing how quickly we appear to heal. It's like a woman going through the agony of childbirth and less than a year later doing it all again. There is something inside us that can erase the pain. Denial is a very powerful element. It burrows deep into your ego and anchors itself there, resisting the weight of evidence, logic and qualified argument to dislodge it. A distinguished professional had reasonably told me that I was suffering from bipolar disorder, but I believed he was wrong. It would take at least two months before those pillars of denial would begin to fragment and finally disintegrate. That ultimate acceptance of reality, recognising the illness and that it needed to be managed just like any other infirmity, would be a monumental bridgehead in the healing process. Pretending that it didn't exist, that I couldn't possibly be hard-wired that way, was self-defeating. Acceptance is one small step on the long journey to self-knowledge. In this process, I was helped by reading about relaxation, meditation and alternative life philosophies. Running through these texts were the themes of ego and humility. For me to accept Dr Safranco's diagnosis, my ego would have to vacate the driving seat.

Ego can destroy. At our most desperate point in life, our ego will not save us. It is not a building block. It is an intangible that cannot be sustained. Even though I was absolutely destroyed, a tiny spark of my ego continued to burn in the dark. After all I had been through, that granule of ego continued to resist by refusing to let me accept that I needed help. It hung on, telling me that I could still get out of my predicament. It is illogical, enmeshed with the survival instinct, and it doesn't want to let go. This was a battle which had to be fought between two opposing sides within me. Thank God, the right side won. My ego had been the agent which had refused to allow me to concede that something was seriously wrong. And, to hold that position, my ego fought almost to the very death – my death.

The example of others who have struggled would be a great source of inspiration over the long months of my recovery. Since the breakdown I have read the Dalai Lama, the Bible, works of the eastern mystics, autobiographical accounts of bipolar sufferers and many texts on healing and meditation. I'm still reading. It's been part of an extensive but very necessary process of soul searching.

Ultimately, enough clues came across my line of sight to convince me that the sooner this tough reality was confronted, the better the chance of my recovery. It compelled me to undertake a detailed analysis of the years leading up to my breakdown. This archaeological dig of the psyche took me back a full fifteen years – a stretch of time littered with enough evidence to force me to admit that I had been ignoring the warning signs all along. Yes, I had been a binge drinker. What about those nights when ideas had been occurring at such electrifying speed that I would jump out of bed and churn out page after page of notes? Didn't that point to mania and an elevated mood?

The archaeological dig found no evidence back in my teenage years but there were distinct signs through my early twenties and stronger indications as time moved on. Taking those reference points and comparing them with the recognised symptoms of bipolar showed a definite correlation. Before long I was painting in the blank spaces as I recollected the massive low points of depression and the cyclonic bouts of mania. Working my way down the list of symptoms, all the way to grand delusions and psychosis, it became a simple matter of ticking the boxes to arrive at the same conclusion as Dr Safranco. Craig Hamilton, you have bipolar disorder.

Among the sedimentary layers of my forensic dig were 1991 and 1995, two high-water mark years when I definitely should have paid heed to the warning signs.

The first tap on the shoulder happened when, in an attempt to revive its flagging fortunes, Newcastle City Cricket Club had invited me to take on the job as captain-coach starting in 1991. It was a flattering approach. I was probably at the peak of my form during a year in which I would play for New South Wales Country against the touring Sri Lankans at Grafton. I felt strong and confident.

City had finished last the previous summer and had not made the semi-finals since 1975, when David Fordham had played in the team. Like me, David had kicked off his media career as an ABC part-timer before he carved out a national profile as a sports reporter, presenter and commentator on commercial television. Perhaps the City club management identified some talismanic quality in the media connection. I'd always enjoyed the leadership role and had undertaken the captaincy for quite a few teams in rugby and cricket as I graduated through the various grades. But Belmont had proven a different proposition. Blessed by a strong core of senior players, the club was well stocked when it came to potential leaders. Belmont didn't need me as captain whereas Newcastle City did. Skippering the Belmont under-23s had whetted my appetite but, if I was going to lead a first-grade side, I would have to switch clubs. I shook hands on the Newcastle deal, determined to do a good job.

The move entailed a significant cultural shift. Whereas the Belmont boys were very much a mixture of white and blue collar (including a few coalminers), City was considered a port for professional types like accountants and solicitors. In fact, the approach to me had been made by two solicitors, one of whom was the outgoing club captain Peter Chapman.

My first contribution was enticing Belmont clubmate Greg Hook to join me and we were immediately impressed by the enthusiasm and commitment of the squad during the early matches. As spring gave way to the summer of 1991–92, it was apparent we were building a competitive outfit. Each sign of improvement fuelled my determination to achieve more. In the last premiership game of the season we had to beat – guess who? Belmont – to make the semis. They won the toss and batted and we knocked them over for 248 – not a great score but still eminently defendable. The run chase the following Saturday would deliver one of the proudest days of my sporting life. Our opening batsmen, Scott Carlin and Andrew Sargent, both made hundreds. We were none for 200 and the first wicket didn't fall until tea – 16 runs away from victory. Gary Onslow walked to the wicket, smacked four fours and it was all over. From last to third in the space of a year. We pulled up to the bar at The Junction Tavern and partied like there was no tomorrow.

There may have been no tomorrow, but there was a next week. And guess who we met in the semi-final? Belmont. Our victory the previous Saturday had given us a great deal of self-belief and we went into the game knowing that we wouldn't die wondering. City made 299. It would take a good side to score 300 to beat us. And Belmont were a good side. It was a great contest. We scrapped hard all the way, taking seven wickets before they reached the target. The City boys weren't destined to make the final but by any definition it had been a fabulous summer.

Unlike an over-fuelled boiler or high-revving motor, there is no gauge to tell humans when to back off. Throughout that year I had been working full-time in the mine, part-time for the ABC, starting a family and throwing whatever I had left into the captain-coach assignment with my new club. The amazing aspect of the mania component of bipolar disorder is that it offers seemingly limitless reserves of energy. This explains, in part, why some of the greatest achievers of the ages have been manic depressives. Like windsurfers scudding on a howling sea breeze they have managed to ride the mania as a force for creative output. Winston Churchill, who packed about four lives into one, was an absolute workaholic until what he called The Black Dog – the depressive part of the illness – would descend and he would retreat to the bottle or bed.

If I had possessed the insight, the warning signs would have been self-evident. It took three or four games into the 1992-93 season for me to hit the wall. The energy was gone. It would be my last season of cricket. I visited my doctor wondering whether I was suffering glandular fever, burnout or just plain exhaustion. He gave me a certificate indicating 'viral illness' and prescribed eight weeks off work. He also referred me to a psychiatrist but, by the time I made the consultations, my symptoms weren't so severe, resulting in the conclusion that my condition was simply exhaustion and burnout brought on by a frenetic lifestyle. I returned to work having learned nothing. It could have been the wake-up call I so desperately needed, but I missed the clues.

My next big tap on the shoulder occurred in 1995. Once again, it was a matter of loading way too much on the one plate. Terry Fernie, the mining union's lodge president at Stockton Borehole Colliery, was leaving the mine and the union was looking for a suitable replacement. As check inspector or safety officer I was never backward in taking on management over safety issues. The biggest blues were usually over the issue of dust. This is why guys who worked in the British mines and migrated to Australia ended up with black lung, a killer disease caused by fine dust particles. We knew all about the problem but there was still this attitude from mine management of 'we'll get away with what we can because production is paramount'. If watering or salting a road, or installing better ventilation systems, was going to slow production, management and union would butt heads. As safety officer, I relished the responsibility of going toe-to-toe with the bosses. That reputation plus my ability to address a meeting made me a logical candidate to take over as lodge president and join delegates from mines throughout Australia at the three-day national mining union conference on the Gold Coast.

Within a day of arriving at the conference, I didn't feel well. It wasn't a matter of too much hospitality because I stayed right away from drink and late nights. The batteries were just about dead at a time when I needed to be at my best in a position of new responsibility. It was such a relief to arrive back home where I immediately applied for a couple of weeks off work. Yet again, I had failed to identify the pattern of mania-burnout-collapse. Two significant cues – 1991 and 1995 – both went unheeded. It was three strikes and you're out.

As they say, what doesn't kill you makes you stronger. My first two warnings were hiccups. They left me with enough strength to have booked myself in for assistance. I didn't. Instead, I had to hit absolute bottom where, rather than having the option of walking into a waiting room and sitting down for an appointment, what was left of the mess had to be metaphorically scraped off the pavement.

The perch from which I would ultimately fall was about as lofty a roost as I could find: opening week of the Olympic Games. Was this the time when I would be the most vulnerable? Why did it come to such a cataclysmic head on that train station at that time? Was it the big gig which pushed me over the edge? I don't know for sure, but I suspect not. My conviction is that the timing was merely a monumental coincidence. It was going to happen sometime. My guess is the fact that it happened on a railway station on the way to the Olympics with a pass around my neck just shows that God has a sense of humour.

My first recognition of the downslide was that awful New Year's Eve of 1999. The fact that it took another eight or nine months for the drama to end in that burning tailspin of September 2000 was purely a matter of destiny.

I remain convinced that my cards were marked with the certainty that a breakdown was going to occur – sooner or later. Fate chose the place and date.

Accepting my illness gave me a starting point. Since that event, I wake every day and automatically run a check of my well-being – ask myself how I'm feeling. Am I a little bit up today? Am I a bit down? Like a surf lifesaver watching the area between the flags, I'm eternally vigilant for the rips, sinking sandbanks and telltale fins of peril. It's an important ritual in the process of maintaining self-awareness. After so long ignoring the obvious, I don't want to get ambushed again. The outcomes are too catastrophic. If I was a piece of mining machinery, there would be indicators displaying the pressure levels. A turn of the wheel here, a release of that valve there, a bit of topping up with that lubricant, and all the dials are back to where they should be, functioning sweetly. Humans aren't machinery. We don't have dials. For that reason we must pay heed to what our inner prompts are telling us. Put ego aside, ignore the propaganda of your self-image as the unbreakable Australian superhero and *listen to those inbuilt indicators*.

Since my breakdown I have been active in mental health awareness campaigns, partly because before my crash I was totally convinced that there was nothing on my horizon capable of bringing such calamity to my family. Hey, I was the sanest, most together bloke I knew. I was so cocksure nothing could happen to me. Life was good. It couldn't happen, but it did. The year 2000 could have cost me my job, my marriage, my friends, my family and my life. When you come out the other side and the fog clears from your goggles, it occurs to you that maybe one of the reasons you survived was so that you could inform others. My experience tells me there must be thousands of people out there choosing to ignore the warning signs until it is too late.

One of the most liberating aspects of my recovery is that I have discovered the ability to say no. First, I had to admit to myself that I had a mood disorder and that I had contributed significantly to that problem by my innate inability to say no. Simply, I had a dreadful habit of taking on way more than I needed. For a bloke who had spent all his life saying yes, finding an alternative wasn't easy. It has taken some discipline. Whereas I had been the sort of person who would say, 'Sure, just leave it with me,' now I had to pause, take a breath, stay calm and say: 'I have enough on my plate at the moment, so I'll have to say no.' It was very strange.

Conceding the existence of bipolar disorder was a breakthrough. I was no longer swimming against the tide of logic. This impression was reinforced during my subsequent visit to Dr Safranco. He appeared satisfied with my progress, checked that I was still taking my daily dose of Epilim, reiterated its importance in stabilising my mood and concluded by telling me that I wouldn't have to make another appointment. Happily, as doctor and patient, we were done.

Three months or so had elapsed since the breakdown and although Dr Safranco's involvement was over, I wouldn't be performing entirely without a safety net. Our family doctor had placed me under the watchful eye of psychiatrist Dr Alan Weiss. If I had been feeling isolated in my experience as a mental health patient, my contact with Dr Weiss instantly told me I wasn't alone. The demand for his services was so great that his waiting list ran into months. The fact that psychiatrists have more patients than they can handle goes to the heart of the great mystery: how have we managed to hide mental health away from society when it is obviously such a major issue? If you doubt it, try getting in to see a psychiatrist. Obviously, governments are very good at ignoring such realities which explains, in part, why Australia's expenditure on mental health is half that of New Zealand, Britain, Canada and the United States. So, we have this terrible situation of the family bearing the brunt of a problem which society is convinced doesn't exist. I was one of the fortunate ones. Not only did the fall into the abyss not kill me, but I had great family, wonderful friends, a sympathetic employer and so many other elements to help my recovery. Very few others are so lucky. As one of the fortunate few I feel duty-bound to speak out.

10

LINES IN THE RIVER

W hen the tide rips the world out from under your feet and sweeps you on floodwaters in full torrent, how do you survive? The surge bears all before it as you flounder, groping helplessly for branch, twine or trailing line – anything that might arrest your momentum and haul you to sanctuary.

How did I survive? Out of my line of sight, family, friends and mental health professionals gathered at intervals on the riverbank to cast trailing lines in my path in the hope that I might snag any or all to be hauled clear of the deluge. They saved my life.

Shining with the glow of unstinting love was Louise. Later in the book, I have devoted a separate chapter to my life partner and her role in my salvation. Farther down the bank was the team of psychiatric professionals who would not only oversee my retrieval from the flood, but manage my recovery. Standing alongside Louise and the professionals were my family and best friends. Among them a collection I've called the Magnificent Seven – not dwarfs but giants as far as friendship and loyalty are concerned. They too, threw the collective lifeline and hauled me from oblivion.

I can't tell you how to survive a mental breakdown. None of us is exactly the same as the next person and I suspect our circumstances vary in so many ways. Some people are swept into the stream and never make it out, floundering there forever. Others drown. What I can tell you is that in the singular experience of Craig Hamilton going crazy, my friends were there to help bear me back to the shore.

The Magnificent Seven are my mates, most of whom I have known since primary school. Generally, we Australian men don't bare our souls to each other. For us, much remains unspoken. It is the understanding of these unspoken bonds that really define mateship. Barry Smith and I had known each other since we were about eight or nine. From that time we had been mates and sporting colleagues. Midway through 2000, when I was mired in depression, Barry was one of the people I had phoned to say, 'Mate, I don't know what is happening here. I'm struggling and you might have to give me a bit of time and space. If I don't ring you or I appear evasive, please understand that I'm doing it tough and trying to work out what is going on with me.'

The call to Peter Dunn was similar. My first memories of Peter date back to when the local Catholic school and Singleton High were thrown together in the same hall for our Higher School Certificate exams. Peter was from the Catholic school and occupied the table next to me. We were doing the same paper and it was obvious we were both struggling. Similarly confounded by the questions, we looked up, caught each other's eye and laughed. It was one of those rare moments and we have shared many better ones since.

After school Peter became part of a circle that included Greg Moore, Barry Smith, Andrew Shaddock and me. It all started with a bunch of mates having a few beers together and something funny would happen to set us off. Similar whacko senses of humour fed off each other and after a while we decided to work these routines into sketches to record on video camera. We called it The Whip in honour of one of our mates, Peter Bull. Peter's nickname was The Whip so we dedicated our get-togethers to him.

From a rough beginning, we started to have real fun and in Greg found ourselves a genius at DIY video editing. We'd mimic rock videos or TV shows of the time (complete with car chases), game shows, the Channel Nine cricket commentary, press conferences and produce loosely scripted skits – anything for a laugh. It was great fun and a relief for a bunch of school-leavers who had suddenly found themselves in coalmining, carpentry and real estate and were looking for an outlet from the workaday world they had just entered. It all culminated in a big night at the Singleton

Rugby Club for what we called The Whip Dinner. The program featured special awards and lucky door prizes, best performance in a leading role plus a best and fairest. The prize for the lucky door draw was a cupboard door. It was that sort of show. If somebody had rolled his car or gone DUI (or both), he'd get a trophy. If a girl had broken up with three boyfriends in the same year, we'd give her an award. It was like the Oscars coming to Singleton. The big trophy was an empty KB beer can mounted on a wooden base, but the real highlight of the evening was the showing of The Whip video. Everybody knew all the in-jokes of the time because it was based on the gossip and go-round of a country town.

The boys had only envisaged it lasting one year but the first show was such an outrageous success, we had to go again. By year two, The Whip Dinner had become a sell-out. We did it for three years and it became the hottest ticket in town and a very entertaining night. As mates, it cemented our friendships. All of us associated with the project were already very close, but became closer via the shared experience. When we broke up as a group to pursue careers and marriages, we still kept in regular contact.

One of the guest players in The Whip had been Scot Leighton. He hadn't been part of the inner production circle but Scot is not the sort of bloke you can leave out of anything. We met in Year 3 at Hunter Street Public School in Singleton and knocked around together. Before we heard the expression 'naturally gifted athlete' we already knew Scot could out-run, jump, throw or swim everybody else.

Without a shadow of a doubt he is the greatest smart-arse I've ever met in my life – a cynic nonpareil. If being a smart-arse was an Olympic event, Scot would have been a triple gold medallist. His humour is lightning quick and often delivered with an abrasive edge. Never have I known anybody to get the better of him in a verbal joust. He was a challenge and I was immediately attracted to him. We drifted apart in the early years of high school but in the senior years we were as thick as ever.

Part of the glue was our love of sport. We toured New Zealand with the school rugby side in 1978 and played together for Singleton. Scot was way ahead of me in ability, playing first grade centre while he was still in school, the same year he made the Australian under-17 team in the company of the likes of Michael Lynagh. My understanding is that the future Wallaby skipper was one of the many who believed Scot could have gone all the way as a rugby international. But my mate was never a great trainer, preferring a smoke or a beer to flogging himself around the training paddock. He enjoyed a good time. He was on the bench for New South Wales Country when they played Scotland at Singleton and should have got a game. There was only one Singleton bloke in the squad, Scotland were winning and, to the absolute disgust of the home crowd, the Country coach declined to give the local lad a run.

Scot was a fair cricketer, too. He left Reedy Creek-Warkworth to join our mob at Glendon and we enjoyed great success together as a pair of quick bowlers and lower order batsmen. The only sport at which he doesn't excel is golf and he gives that most difficult of games a wide berth. Like me, he went into the mining game as a trainee, qualified for his deputy's ticket and later gained undermanager's qualifications. As if we didn't have enough in common, six months after I started going out with Louise, he asked her younger sister Christine out on a date. Scot and Christine might have starting dating after us, but they beat Louise and me to the altar. Today, they're married with two kids. The joke at our wedding was that Scot and I married sisters so we could spend more time together.

When I moved down to Newcastle, Scot remained in the Valley working below ground in Electricity Commission mines and playing rugby for Singleton and later the powerful Maitland club where he won a couple of premierships, typically winning one trophy by kicking the deciding field goal. Family holidays, get-togethers and festive seasons with the Kelly gang meant we saw plenty of Scot. We were tight.

I didn't ring him about the depression. A Kelly family barbecue at Scot and Christine's place coincided with my time off work during the winter of 2000. It was a Saturday, a day when I should have been at a far-flung football field sideline-eyeing for the ABC. Instead, I was as enervated as warmed-over roadkill, slumped with the passenger seat cranked back while Louise drove us to Singleton for what should have been a happy occasion. My presence there, rather than on ABC duty, would require an explanation. The entire Kelly clan was gathered on the back deck but the bloke who earned a quid by talking to radio audiences around the land didn't have the words or the energy to face them. While I headed indoors to find a quiet, dark corner, Louise imparted the news to her family. 'Craig's depressed, he's doing it tough, he's not very well at all,' was how she put it.

Scot wandered in on his own and I buttonholed him for a one-on-one. 'I've got nuthin',' I began. 'I've got no energy. I'm totally exhausted. I've never been so flat in all my life. I don't know why I'm depressed. They've got me on medication to get me out of it, but nothing seems to be working.'

He didn't reply. I chanced a look at my mate, this cynical, smart-arsed rogue who had never been stuck for a word in his life. I was rocked by what I recognised in his eyes. Fear. It wasn't a selfish emotion but rather a momentary terror sparked by his recognition of my pitiful desperation. And, instantly, the look passed. He understood the gravity of the circumstances. 'Fine, okay,' said Scot. 'We'll get you through it.'

It was the assurance I needed. I followed him outside and was immediately embraced by the understanding of the family. They knew I needed space and simply invited me to do whatever made me the most comfortable that afternoon. And, for me, that meant lying down somewhere quiet and doing nothing. Later, Graham, Louise's younger brother, chose his moment to ask: 'What is it? Is it a physical or a mental thing?'

Good question. My answer was that it felt like a bit of both. My body was tired, feeble and sore but I was also suffering from anxiety and a mental torment. The truth was,

I really didn't know what I was dealing with. Now, I understand that the process involves adjusting the serotonin levels in the brain. As a family, we knew nothing about the nature of mental illness. The next few years would be an education for us all. If I had to select a point at which I felt I was starting to claw my way out of the swamp of depression, I would nominate that afternoon at Scot's place. You have to start somewhere. Scot was the first of the seven.

———

The year 2000 found Greg Moore in the United States. I hadn't seen Andrew Shaddock for a while but realised I needed to talk to my mates and phoned Barry Smith and Peter Dunn. You don't make such a call without a bit of soul-searching. Everybody has his own cares and woes in this world. Did they need to be shouldering mine as well? Should I be dumping this burden on them? After all this time, I remain more convinced than ever about the value of that age-old wisdom: a burden shared is a burden halved. If you are in desperate straits, tell your friends. Communicate. Reach out. Share the story. Do not go as long as I did with nothing but your own counsel. Many fortunate folk travel through life without ever being buffeted by the storm. But, if the tempest ever wrecks your voyage, pray that you have taken the time to nurture true friendships. You will need them.

I rang Barry and Peter. They were two and three of the seven. Number four was my wicketkeeper mate Peter Schacht. 'Caught Schacht bowled Hamilton' had been a familiar line in Belmont Cricket Club scorebooks for ten years and our synergy away from the game had been just as sweet. I moved on to Newcastle City and he eventually joined Merewether but our friendship prevailed over any distance. He took my phone call and offered understanding and support. The same came from the fifth name on my list, Wayne Fowler, my one-time rival from the Charlestown club turned great mate courtesy of that Cavaliers tour of the UK. The sixth was Grant Rodgers, my mate from day one at Stockton Borehole Colliery. He knew enough about me to appreciate I was really struggling and he simply pledged his support and understanding. Tom Hoppe, another longtime cricketing mate from Belmont Cricket Club, was the seventh.

This tight circle of true friends took the news of my problems with a degree of forbearance. For those closest to me, it was perhaps toughest on the Hamilton family, particularly our sister Kate. As the elder brother I had never really encountered any setbacks. Like an ice-breaking ship, I had cut an uninterrupted swathe, sweeping life's challenges out of the way with consummate ease, towing my siblings in my wake. Nobody had expected the lead ship to sail off the end of the earth. This was disconcerting. Mental illness can be more difficult for the family than it is for the patient. My parents and siblings handled it by embracing me without judgement or question. Their love was a constant.

I must emphasise here that we are talking about the period from early to mid 2000 when I was in the grip of a depressive illness. Nobody, least of all friends and family, had a glimpse of the mountains of mania lurking on the other side of the great depression. Although I had told everybody who needed to know, I had spared them the full black detail of the depths of my depression. Like a terribly confronting movie, that dark truth would require its own rating, warning of its capacity to shock and frighten. My loved ones didn't need the full surround-sound, in-your-face ugliness of it all. Knowing that I was ill and trying to fight my way back with their help was enough.

Another who supported me throughout was Paul Harragon. Our paths had first crossed at Cahill Oval, Belmont, home ground of our cricket club and Lakes United rugby league side from where The Chief had been recruited by the Knights. Next to the oval stands Belmont Sportsman's Club and, to gain entry in those days, you may have had to pass the quiet scrutiny of a towering young doorman in the form of Paul Harragon. We knew each other. As a commentator I had been on hand for almost his entire National Rugby League career. I was there to record the moment in 1997 when he hoisted the grand final trophy and made one of the most inspirational off-the-cuff acceptance speeches ever. He engendered respect. After his playing career he became one of the busiest people I know, but when I called him three days before my stint on the Madeleine Randall show, he dropped everything and met me for coffee.

'Chief,' I started, 'I want to ask you something.'

'Yep,' he invited.

'Who would be the last bloke you would think of, six or seven weeks ago, was contemplating suicide?'

He named two people and, without batting an eyelid, queried: 'You?'

Between the coffee mugs and sugar sachets I laid out the nightmare of the previous months and told him of my determination to publicise the issue on air. He told me what I had been through was a test.

'We all get 'em,' he said. 'What's important is how you respond.'

You can draw strength from people like Paul Harragon as he had drawn strength from his own family. His dad Harold had been a coalminer whose career had ended when an industrial accident wrecked his back. But Harold hadn't let the pain and discomfort of the condition cloud his vision of what was possible for his children. I had grown to recognise Paul as something more than a bloke who had got lucky enough to win a premiership. He was an inspiration in his own right. Many weeks later, after that crash on Broadmeadow station, Randall McMurphy and The Chief caught up again for part two of the gentle pep talk on prevailing over life's adversities. Like the members of the Magnificent Seven, he was a pillar in my struggle.

At times I exercise my mind about just how all these friends viewed my troubles and their cameos in the drama. For instance, what must it have been like for Peter Schacht and Wayne Fowler on that dreadful day when they visited me at James Fletcher? Put yourself in their shoes — what do you wear when you are going to visit a mental patient? There they were in the sanctity of their family homes, buttoning shirts, tying laces, picking up car keys, preparing for a journey they could never have imagined they would make. Through the confronting process of the Waratah Wing's high-security systems they were ushered, dampening down their disquiet; two decent blokes doing their best not to appear alarmed. What must they have thought when they witnessed my facial contortions triggered by the Serenace? They must have been wondering where their mate had gone and whether he was going to return. Yet, throughout my recovery and the ensuing years I've never noticed the slightest flicker to indicate that they have altered their perceptions of me. Their support and friendship have been as constant as the sea breeze in summer.

Chris Williams was exactly the same. Here was the man I inadvertently attempted to traumatise beyond belief when I ambushed him on Broadmeadow station. But the bloke we nicknamed Jelly unhesitatingly presented himself at James Fletcher Hospital as one of my early visitors. Chris was the very essence of understatement, brushing aside the entire Broadmeadow incident as if it was just another bad day at the office.

Despite the buckets of abuse I'd thrown at him at the station, there wasn't the slightest trace of negativity in his manner. He would continue to visit and both he and Kathy remained among my strongest supporters throughout the recovery. It's a terrible turn of events to suffer a breakdown, but I am still astonished at the incredible fortune I encountered in having them at hand on the day to help cushion my tumble. The entire train of events was assisted by so many elements falling in my favour rather than against me. Chris was there to watch over me. Kathy was on hand to make that crucial call for Louise to return. I can't imagine what might have transpired had they not been there to cast a safety net under me as I went into my hideous tailspin. Luck and good friendships were smiling on me.

Tom Hoppe was an opening bowler who had left Charlestown to join Belmont where he became good mates with Peter Schacht and me. As a trio we enjoyed clubbing and catching bands. If there was a midweek beer to be had after training, Tommy was always on the tour with us. As we all grew older, married and mellowed, Tom remained a great mate. He was on a different tour when he lobbed in with Chris for a visit to James Fletcher. It was wonderful to see him and gratifying to note his concern for my welfare. Like the rest of the boys, he was rock solid.

I should point out that the patient was anything but bereft and woebegone. The manic high was of such towering proportions that I was still very elevated and in the early stages of deep denial about the true nature of my illness. The visiting mates confronted a bloke who wasn't depressed, but was certainly confused. By day five or six he was feeling fine and wanted to go home. I was still seriously mentally ill. Initially, I was in no state to truly understand what my friends had to offer when they rallied at the news of my breakdown. But now, knowing that they were *there* means everything to me. Mental illness can be very scary and confronting for friends and family. Unlike a broken limb or an illness requiring surgery, it is not easy to explain or understand. And, it is stigmatised. I wouldn't have blamed anybody if they had given me a wide berth. Yet, without knowing what the hell was going on with their mate Hamo, the boys rallied to my side. No conditions, no dumb questions, just unequivocal support. My true friends had shown their colours.

The difficult issue for more than half of my friends and family was the false dawn. They had seen me in the grip of the depression of mid-2000 and had reason to believe I was out of the woods, back on the trail to the Olympics. Then came the news of my breakdown at Broadmeadow and the hospitalisation. As I mentioned earlier, Barry and Donna Smith with their kids Jenna, Gabe, Cale and Keely had been on their way to our place for Sunday lunch when they had listened to my unadulterated exposé of depression on the Madeleine Randall show. They had been shocked at the news that I had been suicidal. Barry would later say that he knew something was very wrong that day but he could not have realised that I was in the upper stages of mania. Two days later I would have my massive breakdown and people like Barry and Donna would have to reassess everything we had discussed that Sunday in the light of this awful turn of events. It would have been enough to make lesser people run a mile, but they stuck fast.

There had been many phone calls in the wake of my on-air rendering of my fight with depression. One who delayed his call to the following day was Greg Arms, my former Newcastle representative captain and a figurehead of cricket in the region. In the most heartfelt way Greg expressed his shock and sorrow at learning just how low I had been.

'It's all right, Armsy,' the manic me said reassuringly. 'I'm over it now, mate. I'm on the mend.'

The next day I was in a mental hospital and Greg would join the company of friends confounded and shocked by the turn of events. To their eternal credit, none turned away.

In the weeks following my discharge everybody was on eggshells wondering whether I was going to be okay. Nobody in our circle had ever been hospitalised with a mental illness and if people were treading warily it was perfectly understandable. Their caution was an indication of how much they cared and was conveyed in almost every word and deed. The glaring exception, of course, was the irreverent jokester Scot Leighton. With the sort of mock seriousness only he can muster Scot would remind me that I could 'crack at any time!' Then, with rising alarm in his voice he would warn others: 'Stay back! Stay back! You know what he's capable of. He's dangerous when he's riled!'

It was like the don't-mention-the-war episode of *Fawlty Towers*. Scot not only mentioned the war, he invited me to join it. Not knowing whether to laugh or cry at this sort of therapy, I answered: 'Look, *I* have documentation which says I'm crazy. What's *your* excuse?' It would take much more than a mental breakdown on my part to change Scot. And I wouldn't want it any other way. Had he come over all warm and touchy-feely at my predicament, then I would have known I was in real deep trouble.

The most odious chore for those closest to me was the constant questioning from well-meaning associates: 'What happened to Craig?' As I said earlier, explaining a severed limb or heart bypass surgery is relatively fundamental. But mental illness is much more complicated. Firstly, who wants to admit that a member of their family has gone mad? Secondly, mental illness is such an elusive condition that it is very difficult to explain to a lay person in simple terms exactly what is going on with the patient. It's a bit like shadow boxing with ghosts. If you have had a limb reconstruction, the orthopaedic surgeon will give you a pretty accurate read on how long it will take before you are up and about again. Not so with mental illness. You'll never hear a psychiatrist say: 'If he takes the medication and gets plenty of bed rest, there is no reason why he won't be as good as new in a couple of months.'

The news of my Broadmeadow burnout was all over town in no time. On the day after my admission to hospital, my brother Ian was riding in a Newcastle taxi when, in a phone conversation with his secretary, he delivered an update on my situation. When the call ended, the cabbie piped up:

'I don't mean to pry, but how do you know that bloke?'

'He's my brother,' said Ian.

'Well, I was at the Broadmeadow taxi rank when the police were grappling with him,' the driver continued.

'Oh, yeah?'

'He fought pretty hard. I don't reckon he'd have much skin left on his elbows or knees!'

So it wasn't easy for Ian and Kate. When asked 'What happened to your brother?' they didn't know what to say because they didn't have the answers.

It wasn't funny at the time but now it makes me laugh. There was Ian trying to run his own insurance and investment business in Singleton and doing his best to get on with his life while well-meaning folk were constantly interrupting him to ask what had happened to his brother. You couldn't blame them. The Hamilton boys, just sixteen months apart in age, had been almost inseparable from day one. People always viewed us as brothers, rather than independent entities. But as young adults we had forged our own paths, Ian playing first grade rugby league for the Singleton Greyhounds and Denman before moving on to southern Queensland and winning a premiership with the Southport club. He had returned to his home town to construct a good life which by September 2000 had been rudely interrupted by his brother's predicament. In response to the umpteenth query about my welfare, Ian attempted a different strategy. Instead of massaging the inquisitor's sensibilities with another euphemistic account of my troubles, he announced: 'Look, he's gone mad and he's in hospital!'

From that point the queries eased to a trickle.

11

FRIENDS AND LOVERS

People change. Like stones tumbling down the bed of a stream, we're polished and abraded by the passage of our lives. The years and experiences of adulthood have definitely changed me. But Louise, the impervious rock, hasn't changed. She is the one absolute constant.

Nurses rise from that minority of people who truly care about others. You can't become a career nurse without compassion – the nature of the work is simply too confronting, the need for tolerance too great. Nurses are the good in our society. They look after those who can't look after themselves. Louise was always unequivocal in her career choice: she was going to be a nurse. There was a tradition of service in the Kelly family with aunts who had become nuns.

Louise, the girl I would marry, became a nurse. Three children and a lifetime of experience later she is still proud to be part of the calling. Her colleagues tell me they enjoy working with her and say that she is very good at her job. I don't doubt it.

The key to our great partnership was the fact that we were good friends before we became lovers. I was attracted to her from a distance before she had even worked out who I was. At first she had me confused with another bowler in our cricket team. The fact that the other bloke had a crop of curly red hair, was three years older and looked nothing like me was a bit disconcerting.

My first real glimpse of her was at Howe Park cricket nets where we were practising while she was playing touch football. I turned to Barry Smith and said: 'Jeez, I could marry that girl.' In the old Aussie vernacular, she was a good sort. Had I known she was Pat Kelly's daughter I certainly wouldn't have been game to utter something so bold. After all, I was in Year 12 and she was still in Year 10.

It didn't dawn on me that Louise was Pat's daughter until she started turning up to watch our cricket matches. My team-mates smartly realised that I was pretty keen on her. We'd always go back to the Royal for a few drinks after cricket. One Saturday afternoon, on a prearranged signal, everyone bolted, leaving the two of us together. Louise always thought that I had set it up but that was never the case. It was the boys' doing and I have half an idea that Pat might have been in on it too. My guess is that he had reasoned that if anybody was going to keep his daughter company, better it be somebody who he could keep an eye on; someone nice and close – within swinging distance.

Instead of tripping over our teenage ineptness, we found we conversed with ease. A couple of weeks later our skipper Ian Hodge wed his fiancée Julie and we gathered under a marquee in their back yard for the reception, all of us that is with the exception of Pat, who had only just arrived as a member of the Glendon club. But that didn't stop him and his family from dropping around to pay their respects to the bride and groom. 'Can't stay long,' said Pat, 'got the family in the car.' Well, bring them in, chorused the party gang. And with that I was dispatched to fetch Sue and the Kelly kids. There had obviously been a comment or two passed in my absence because shortly after my return with Louise and her siblings in tow, Roger Worms, one of Singleton's better golfers, remarked: 'So, Pat, this is the girl Hamo's keen on?'

It took me a couple of weeks to work up the courage to ask her out. It was a dilemma I workshopped with Scotty Leighton and the boys at the Royal: 'Should I just go and ask her out, or what? No, she's Pat's daughter, I'd better ask him first.'

When the Kelly family answered the front door of their Wakehurst Crescent home to my tremulous knock, the first thing I noticed was that they were all wearing the same knowing smile. They understood the purpose of my visit. After the small talk was out of the way I discovered Louise had an appointment to keep. Hey, I had Mum's car warmed up at the kerb. 'Why don't I give you a lift?' On the way

I popped the idea that we could go out somewhere together, soon.

On the twelfth of December 1980 we dined at the Lotus Garden Chinese restaurant in Maitland before downing a couple of lemon squashes at Maitland Leagues Club and catching the feature at Rutherford drive-in. As a first date it was so delightfully unsophisticated. And it was wonderful.

We weren't exactly childhood sweethearts, but it was pretty damn close. I was only a couple of weeks away from starting work in Newcastle and Louise had two years of schooling to complete at St Catherine's, Singleton. Early Monday mornings, I'd be on the road down to Stockton Borehole Colliery, returning Wednesday evening for my game of touch football with the Clutha Jets, a bunch of young blokes steered around the park by the canny hand of Max White, who had been captain-coach of Singleton before Pat Kelly. Max would lose his life in a below-ground accident and become yet another entry on that heartbreaking wall commemorating the mining dead. The touch footy was a bonus, but the drawcard that kept me coming back was Louise.

Wednesday night was usually dinner at the Kellys. Pat would always joke that I was eating them out of house and home. I'd leave there about ten or so, sleep at Mum and Dad's, then hit the road early for two more days down the mine before returning to Singleton for a weekend of cricket and more time with my girl. That was the routine for two years until Louise completed her Higher School Certificate and arrived in Newcastle to start work at the Mater.

With three girlfriends for company Louise moved into a rented house at Waratah, near the hospital. In that first year of nursing she made great friends, in particular Ann Salvini and Kim Reid, two who would go the distance.

The arrival of my girlfriend in Newcastle coincided with my recruitment to the Belmont Cricket Club. Suddenly, the compulsion to return to Singleton each week had gone. As Australia's sixth largest city, Newcastle came with most of the trimmings – cinemas, restaurants, night life, great pubs and clubs plus *beaches*. As kids from a regional, land-locked town we took none of this for granted. It was a wonderful time to be stepping out into the world.

Most women would deplore the time cricket imposed on their relationship, but Louise had been born into a sports-playing family and was automatically comfortable with the culture and my desire to test myself in a more demanding competition. As often as not, when I was playing on Satur-days, Louise was rostered on to work. Sure, we both missed Singleton but we were adding new friends to our circle, Louise via her workplace and me through Belmont with the likes of Peter Schacht, Wayne Fowler, Tom Hoppe, Chris Williams and Alan Sharp.

The premiership presented some of the best regional cricketers in Australia, players like Greg Arms, Michael Hill, Tim Towers, Robert Dan, Neil Budden, Greg Geise, Mark Curry, Michael Ryan, Steve Christie and Gary Gilmour. After a couple of games in the seconds, I won a spot in first grade to play the University of Newcastle at University Oval. I stood in the field and watched Gary

'Gus' Gilmour, the bloke who just five years before had taken 6-14 in a World Cup, bowl the first over for Belmont. And then they threw the ball to me. I took six wickets on debut. I wondered if life could get any better. It could – I had a date with Louise that Saturday night.

Adrian Adam was a bloke from the New South Wales Central Coast who I had known through representative cricket and was glad to see that he too had moved to Belmont. He opened the batting in the final against Charlestown and Mick Ryan, a bowler quick enough to have stirred up touring West Indians and Englishmen when he played for Northern New South Wales, hit Adrian under the heart in the first over. From the grandstand, we heard the sickening sound of ball on body and saw Adrian collapse on the pitch. By the time the players reached him, he was spitting blood. The ambulance was called and he was carried from the field. The Sunday paper ran the photo of our opening batsman being loaded into the ambulance. By Adrian's side was the first-year nurse Louise Kelly. On opening the paper the next morning, she was horrified to see that somebody had snapped her in the photo. As for Adrian, after they had reinflated his punctured lung and strapped him like a mummy, he miraculously reappeared to resume his innings at No 8 in the order. His heroics weren't enough as we were well beaten.

On my part, I was certain I had found the right partner but was in no hurry to get married. We were still very young and enjoying the freedom of living away from home with a few bob in our pockets. Yet, over the next four years we would increasingly spend more time together. One day when I was visiting Louise at Waratah, our easy conversation steered itself towards the question. We decided to get engaged. The time was right and it was the logical next step. We kept it a secret for a while and even went to Scot and Christine's engagement party without having told anybody else that we had already made the jump.

No sooner was the engagement ring on Louise's finger than we decided to move in together. We rented a near-new two-bedroom unit in Charlestown and were still living there a year later in September 1987 when we were wed at St Patrick's Catholic Church in Singleton, where a succession of Kellys have tied the knot. Ours was a North Queensland honeymoon, flying into Proserpine then hopping via the Whitsundays and Mission Beach, diving on the reef, soaking up the sun, all the way to Port Douglas.

A year later we bought our house in New Lambton, two nervous newlyweds, hand-in-hand at the on-site auction while Graeme Brownlow, a cricketing mate in real estate, did our bidding. With Graeme turning to us and whispering 'Can you afford it?' we watched the price climb to almost ten thousand beyond what we had expected to pay. When the gavel fell for the final time we had bought ourselves a little 'fixer-upper'. I don't kid myself – I am no handyman. It would take fifteen years to complete the renovating project. As happens with young couples, children intervened. It's hard to polish floors and paint ceilings when the pitter-patter of little feet can be heard in the hall.

When Joshua arrived in February 1991, like a gemstone

turning in the light, Louise displayed yet another wondrous quality: the magic of motherhood. But first came the ordeal of childbirth. Her labour began at 3 am on a Saturday morning and I was optimistic that we would welcome our firstborn well before play got underway at Waratah Oval. We arrived at John Hunter Hospital at 9 am, cricket gear in the boot of the car. Late that afternoon, as stumps were pulled at Waratah, there was still no sign of Joshua. By 7 pm I was a spent force. My anxious vigil hadn't helped one bit as the nursing staff led me out into the corridor for a break.

I can understand now why ancient artisans reverently shaped totems like the Venus of Willendorf in tribute to motherhood. Watching a woman go through childbirth is guaranteed to cause the average bloke to recast all his assumptions about the opposite sex. It was a long and difficult birth during which I perceived that my ever-gentle wife was capable of expressing the sort of language I hadn't heard this side of a coalmine. As a farm boy, I might have been accustomed to nature's basic ways, but this was a revelation. With Josh in her arms, Louise was fine and I was crying like a baby.

The birth had been such an ordeal that we were certain Josh would be an only child. But, again I had underestimated the miracle of the life process and the resilience of women. After a comparatively smooth labour, Amy arrived on 4 February 1993. We had a pigeon pair and that was the way it would stay . . . until exactly four years on, the hankering to make it three found us back in the delivery suite welcoming Laura into the world and presenting Amy with a very special birthday present.

With her four Aquarians (me included), Louise made a wonderful mum. Some people struggle with parenting, but her nurturing soul deemed she was born to it.

In the space of a few short years our lives had been transformed from the easy-going idyll enjoyed by a couple of double-income no-kids twenty-somethings. Most couples find kids and a mortgage a big enough bite knowing that they have to chew like blazes to make it work. But my appetite demanded more. Taking on the part-time radio work in addition to my full-time job was the start. Then I saddled up for the captain-coach challenge with Newcastle City. In very quick time we had gone from carefree young couple to over-committed partnership. My burnout of 1991 should have brought me to my senses. Perhaps the reason that it didn't was because we were already committed to a plan. I had told Louise that I didn't want to work in a mine forever and she had backed me in the long-range project to start a media career. We knew it would be tough with me working seven days a week while Louise combined nursing, motherhood and running the home. But we were young and believed it would be a temporary phase until I could make the move from mining to a full-time media career.

Taking on the union job in 1995 was another pallet of bricks on an already overloaded wagon. Again, I ran into the ditch, requiring time off work to recuperate. Like me, Louise didn't read anything into those dark dips of 1991 and 1995. We were both of the opinion that I had overstretched myself and needed a break. Hiccups. Nothing more. Through my malaise she held the family together and, when the patient was feeling stronger, I resumed the same ill-conceived course. Wisdom is hard won. Today, we share a very different view of what those two warnings meant.

My frenetic life blinded me to the obvious: Louise was working her tail off to keep it all together. While I was pinging between mine, studio and playing field, my wife was feeding and bathing tiny kids, preparing the older pair for school, looking after the house, paying the bills, doing all the chores and fitting in a nursing career around these demands to give us a financial safety net if my media dreams didn't come to fruition. Looking at the burden she was shouldering, it was a wonder she didn't have the break-down. I was in the door and out again without catching so much as a glimpse of the size of her commitment. She couldn't have kept it up without knowing that as partners we had both agreed on the goal that would deliver a career in broadcasting. If she had known that it was going to be mining five days a week and broadcasting for two days with no end in sight, she could have packed up and left and nobody would have blamed her. It had to be temporary.

In 1997, I left the pit. The play that gave us the courage to make the leap was a visit to Sandy MacNeil, accountant, financial advisor and one-time international rugby referee. We laid out the Hamiltons' financial landscape and told Sandy what we had in mind. His advice was to take the redundancy payout from the mine and use it to reduce the mortgage. It meant that we weren't going to be able to spend the money on a holiday or anything else, but it was great advice. Moreover, it gave us the green light to make the move. But for Sandy's wise counsel, I'd still be in the pit. Louise was understandably nervous about it all but she was right there beside me lending support in every way.

The same week, I called Dad and said: 'Dick, I'm thinking about leaving the pit.' My guess was that he'd tell me not to take such a risk. Instead, it was the opposite. 'Good on you,' he said. 'I'm glad you're leaving; you can do better.'

Two years later I won the full-time position with the ABC. Louise was over the moon. To come home with a piece of paper that meant a regular wage packet, membership of the ABC superannuation scheme, the security of government employment plus annual holidays was cause for celebration in the Hamilton household. Louise wore the look of a campaigner who had endured every step of the long march to finally reach a cherished destination. As a partnership, we had held hands and run the gauntlet, but we had emerged triumphant. Surely now it would be smooth sailing for the Hamilton household.

Is timing really a phenomenon of coincidence? Or is there something else at play? Just when an inner mechanism might have been telling us that our long ordeal was over, that we were out into clear air with no great hurdles in our path, I began the rapid decline into depression. The year 2000 was me sliding and Louise again having to carry the load.

Life has its own momentum. It doesn't wait for the depressed man to pull himself together. A household has to function, kids have to be fed and taken to school, helped with homework, tucked into bed. Again, the load toppled off the back of the lorry and fell straight into Louise's lap. It must have been dreadful. She had a right to expect some respite. She comes from resilient Irish stock, but how much more could she take without cracking? When not running the home and chasing after the kids she was at work in a vocation which sucks so much compassion, patience and tolerance from its workers that you wonder just how there is anything left to spend on their own families. At home I was a cot case but she had no idea just how serious it was because I hadn't told her. Maybe I'll feel better tomorrow, I kept telling myself. That's what is so insidious about depression – the victim slides into a state of helplessness where they cannot reach out for assistance. The harsh wisdom here is that it is so important for those around the sufferer to identify the warning signs and respond before it gets worse.

Happiness is hard to quantify. In all the studies on the subject, embracing all different cultures and economic circumstances, the one common factor that shines through is the need for humans to feel that they are moving forward. That impression of advancing, no matter how negligible on some counts, is the only identifiable, universal reading for happiness. Louise must have been desperately unhappy. As a couple we had achieved so much together – house, kids, a wonderful marriage. After so much personal investment on her part, our progress had halted and there seemed no way forward – unless she abandoned the mired member of the family and moved on without him. I don't know how or why she stayed throughout that period. Was it the resilient Irish streak carried in the Kelly genes all the way from the Emerald Isle generations ago? Or was it simply a matter of her instinct for compassion prevailing against the odds? Love conquers all.

If the roles had been reversed and I'd been compelled to carry the load, I don't think I could have gone the distance. And I think that is the reality for so many families. They can't make sense of it, they have exhausted all ways to reach the sufferer and there seems no way out. At the end of their tether, they simply revert to survival mode and walk away. Nobody learns anything until something cataclysmic like a suicide occurs. Then the residual guilt runs its poisonous path, destroying what's left of the family. I was lucky. In the face of everything, Louise stayed. She saved our marriage. She kept us together. She saved my life.

12

GOING PUBLIC

When a cattle dog gets hit by an eighteen-wheeler, if he is still alive after the dust settles, he usually crawls off under a building somewhere and hunkers down in a dark place until he either dies or gets well enough to stumble back out into the light. The dog doesn't do a national tour or appear on television warning other dogs about the perils of chasing trucks.

My instincts were different to that old dog. I would ultimately realise that I had an obligation to help fellow sufferers and their families by talking about my own experiences. Don't let this happen to you, or someone close to you – heed the warning signs, was what I wanted to say. But it took me a long while to arrive at that point. For most folk, the prospect of suffering a mental breakdown would be short-listed among the worst of personal catastrophes. If it is awful for the individual, then it was certainly no picnic for my family and close friends. Given my predilection for taking on too much at one time, you could argue that some of it was self-inflicted. But my loved ones had never asked to be dragged along on the journey. Fate had dealt them a cruel hand.

That experience was bound to leave its scars. For those closest to me the desire was to see me recover, right the ship and get on with the rest of our lives in the best way possible. Although hindsight would enable me to see that I had been tapped on the shoulder a couple of times in the preceding years, the breakdown still came as a total surprise – the complete ambush.

Before my crash I had little or no understanding of mental illness and that ignorance had contributed to the seriousness of my breakdown. When first diagnosed with depression, it took me some time and effort before I was strong enough to apply that label to my illness. At the time of my fateful radio appearance on the Madeleine Randall program, I sincerely believed that not only had I conceded the reality of depression, I had actually beaten the illness. Time would tell that depression was only part of the picture. So too with bipolar. When first diagnosed my reaction was fear, wanting to run, not to confront it and certainly not to discuss it with anybody. Despite the best efforts of three psychiatrists I remained in denial, unwilling to admit that I had a disorder. They were mistaken – I didn't have a mental illness, I thought. It wasn't until I took the time to review my life, stepped inside my own existence and started to recognise the patterns of the mood swings, that I came to the conclusion that the experts were right and I was wrong: I did have bipolar disorder and the sooner I came to terms with it, the sooner I would be able to manage my illness.

That realisation came several months after my appearance on air to talk about depression. So, as far as publicising mental health was concerned, I already had dipped one toe in the water. Two days after that radio show I had suffered a full-blown mental breakdown. It was a pretty vicious way of acquainting me with the fact that I had climbed into the ring with an opponent who had a surprise left hook and had just nailed me with it. Once bitten, twice shy.

My priority during those first few months of the breakdown was to be able to return to work with the hope of once again leading a productive, creative and fulfilled life with all my relationships intact. It dawned on me that there would be so many others whose chances of regaining some control over their lives would be next to nil unless they received the sort of assistance and support which had helped rescue me.

David Fairleigh is a giant of a man who played an uncompromising brand of rugby league during his time with North Sydney, Newcastle, New South Wales and Australia. When his playing days were done he showed an aptitude for calling the game and was recruited by the

WHAT IS PSYCHOSIS?

Psychosis can simply be defined as being out of touch with reality. An individual in this state will often display psychotic symptoms like imagining he or she is someone else, that they may be in a different time or place and having little grip on the here and now.

ABC. As a working colleague he has been extremely supportive of me and my efforts to promote awareness of mental health. My experience wasn't his first brush with the subject. At North Sydney, David had been a team-mate of Peter Jackson, a fantastic player who represented both Queensland and Australia. In 1997, Jacko died of a drug overdose, a tragedy which cast light on his troubled existence and his personal battle with depression. David said it was clear during his time at Norths that Jacko was waging a war with his own demons, but nobody knew the particular nature of his ailment. In the tough, self-reliant environment of a football club it is a sign of weakness to admit to such frailty. It wasn't until his lonely death in a cheap motel that it became known that Peter Jackson had been sexually abused as a teenager. On hearing of Jacko's life and his tragic end, I became more determined to shed light on the subject of mental health awareness and, in particular, the hidden costs of depressive illness.

The primary reason I decided to promote mental health

awareness is because I want to help destigmatise the entire process. We are conditioned to avoid mental illness, we're embarrassed by it, and so drop it in the too-hard basket. That attitude has to change. For this reason, people miss out on getting help until they are critical. The fallout is enormous. It costs governments, employers and the entire community. But, worst of all, the human cost for the individual, their families and others close to home can be absolutely devastating. I would view it as a total cop-out if I failed to accept the opportunity to help others. Part of being human is sharing our life experiences. That doesn't mean we talk exclusively about the good things – it's got to be about the bad things as well. We learn from adversity and out of suffering come some of life's most valuable lessons. If we can encourage people to heed the warning signs and seek positive intervention, then maybe we can alleviate some suffering.

Once you make a decision like that it reminds you just how much power each of us can muster and what a difference we can make. Sometimes you have to suffer to realise that you do have that power of choice to refuse to be a victim. It is too easy to pull on the coat of victimhood. You can live your life with an excuse or you can say, 'No, I choose not to be a victim.'

When confronted by adversity, the most important thing of all is how we respond. Yes, bad things happen to good people – that is a sad fact of life. But the real issue is *what you choose to do about it*. The past can teach us many things and hold a treasure-trove of great memories, but we don't live

WHAT IS MANIA?

The term 'mania' refers to the most extreme state of overactivity or elation. The symptoms include an elevated mood in which the person feels extremely high, full of energy and, often, invincible. Speech and thought patterns are more rapid than usual and the person will speak very quickly, often jumping from one subject to the next. In this state, the sufferer has a reduced need for sleep. Another symptom is irritability, often with people who can't follow their rapid thought processes or disagree with their unrealistic ideas.

there. Where we all live is in the here and now. Treasuring the moment is one of the greatest lessons I have learned from my breakdown. During those long weeks off work, these were the issues and choices I was led to confront.

Having an understanding of what this illness can do provided me with incentive to find a way to manage it. Bipolar can destroy your life but if you have the tools to deal with it, you can live a normal existence. As they say, that which doesn't kill you makes you stronger. It almost killed me. But I survived. At the age of thirty-seven I had to learn how to live another way. It has been an amazing education. As awful as it was, my breakdown was the crash I had to have in order to rebuild my life on a better, more durable foundation.

Once you start helping other people, you are helping yourself. If I was going to help others, I had to be strong within myself. The false start of the radio session on depression had taught me a tough lesson. Throughout 2001 I was very tentative. Although I had returned to work and appeared to be coping, the reality was that it would take at least a year before the ground beneath my feet started to feel solid again. To all intents I was moving steadily away from that dreadful place represented by September 2000, but the thought constantly occurred to me that at any time I might have been just a step or two away from the edge of the abyss.

By 2002 I felt my confidence was growing. This time it wasn't the old superficial confidence making a return but rather a new wellspring surging quietly from deep within me. I recognised it as a product of the emerging self-knowledge that had come with my acceptance of my illness and my resultant gradual recovery. With that new-found strength came the question: what do I do with this? Do I quietly get on with my life and try to forget that it ever happened? Or do I use it for the greater good? My thinking might have been influenced by a quote attributed to Martin Luther King: 'Our lives begin to end the day we become silent about things that matter'. By mid-2002 I had my answer.

Around that time Newcastle journalist Chad Watson filed a feature piece on my breakdown and recovery for the weekend magazine section of the *Newcastle Herald*. The story triggered a flood of responses, many from people encountering similar problems within their own families. Some told me that because the subject area was so difficult to broach, they had instigated action by throwing the newspaper – open at Chad's article – on the table with the

WHAT IS BIPOLAR DISORDER?

It used to be called manic depression, but bipolar disorder is a more appropriate description because it depicts the two extremes – or poles – that characterise the illness. Anyone suffering bipolar disorder would be having difficulty experiencing a normal range of mood.

The best way to understand bipolar is to imagine a globe. The point at the top (North Pole) represents the high or the mania. The opposite point (South Pole) is the depression. A sufferer experiencing symptoms of either pole for at least a week is said to be undergoing an episode. Rapid-cycling bipolar disorder occurs with four or more episodes of mania and/or depression in the space of a year.

Bipolar disorder is usually associated with severe mood swings accompanied by changes in the ability to function, physical well-being, emotion and thought processes. The swings are more extreme and enduring than the normal highs and lows we experience in our day-to-day lives. Emotions can run the gamut from feelings of utter helplessness to extreme elation. People usually go through periods of normal mood in between these times.

words, 'Have a look at this.' The article had become a catalyst for changing lives. A fellow I had known for a long time approached me and said, 'I read the story and realised I was going through exactly the same thing. It gave me hope and the inspiration to seek help. It was exactly what I needed at a very critical time.' No doubt there were people out there thinking, why does he have to bare his soul like this? We don't need to know these details about his life. But they weren't the ones who had encountered mental illness; they weren't the ones who needed help.

So great was the positive response to the article that it motivated me to do more. Early in 2003 Stephen Mount, a journalist with NBN Television in Newcastle, called to ask if I would mind talking to a young woman by the name of Julia Page, who was experiencing similar problems. Julia, who works in the wine and food industry, was organising a fundraiser for youth suicide awareness and she asked if I could mention it on my radio show. My response was to not only plug it on air but to suggest that we hold a public forum the night before the event and invite mental health experts and the general public to attend. The proposal was to organise a guest speaker through the John Hunter Hospital Adolescent Psychiatric Unit and for Julia and me to also speak on the night. The forum would be chaired by Madeleine Randall, who was no stranger to the issue and who has great empathy for the subject.

The day before the forum I was on air with Lindy Burns promoting the event and talking about my own experiences with depression. While we were chatting a call came through to our producer Diana Slater. It was from a family man who was suffering severe depression and admitted he was just about at the end of his tether. His duty to work and provide for his family prevented him taking time off,

WHAT ARE THE STAGES OF BIPOLAR DISORDER?

Bipolar disorder comprises four prime episodes. They are mania, hypomania, depression and mixed mood. During a manic episode the sufferer is peculiarly and continuously elevated. His mood may be expansive or irritable and can last at least a week. A hypomanic episode, or hypomania, is a milder form of mania lasting at least four days.

At the other end of the scale is a major depressive episode or what we commonly call depression. It entails a period lasting a fortnight or more during which there is a depressed mood often accompanied by a loss of interest or enjoyment in nearly all activities. During a mixed episode, the bipolar person experiences both poles – mania and depression – nearly every day for at least a week.

admitting his vulnerability and seeking help. He had been depressed for almost three years. On four or five occasions he had felt seriously suicidal. Neither his wife nor his three children knew. The pressure to be the breadwinner overrode any impulse he might have had to call for help. When we came off air Diana had tears in her eyes as she told us about the call and how she had beseeched him, after he had so bravely phoned us, to take the next step and seek proper help. But he had hung up, seemingly in despair, without leaving a name or number.

Me aged four weeks
with Mum and Dad
in Singleton, NSW,
in 1963.

With my brother Ian in Singleton, aged about four. I decided he needed
hosing down – big brothers are always one step ahead.

On the family farm on the outskirts of Singleton with my great mate Bim the border collie.

A couple of famous faces and a bloke in a blazer. New Zealand cricketing great Sir Richard Hadlee and world famous umpire Harold 'Dickie' Bird gladly agreed to be snapped with me while I was touring New Zealand with the Emu Colts cricket side in 1983.

Louise's and my wedding day in 1987, a truly wonderful day spent with family and friends. There is a hero in this story – she's on the right! Without Louise I would never have had the strength to deal with my mental illness.

Batting in the nets at Newcastle representative cricket practice at the University Oval in 1989.

Moments after finishing a shift underground at Teralba Colliery in 1997. Coalmining is a tough way to make a dollar. Six months later I left the industry for good after sixteen years.

Belmont's First Grade premiership winning team, 1990–91 season. I'm second from the right in the front row. The team was captained by Mark Curry (third from the right in the front row). Second from the right in the back row is my wicketkeeping mate Peter Schacht.

Interviewing 'The Chief', Paul Harragon, for ABC Radio after another wholehearted effort for his beloved Newcastle Knights. Paul became a key figure in my recovery, offering tremendous support and guidance when I needed it.

You meet some great characters in the sporting world, and this bloke is one of them. I'm interviewing Brisbane's Allan 'Alfie' Langer after the Broncos had beaten the Canberra Raiders on a cold Saturday night in Canberra.

Taking part in The Newcastle Debate at Newcastle Town Hall in 1999 with well-known Australian actor John Howard (the moderator of the debate). It's funny, most people hate public speaking. I've learnt to relax and enjoy it.

The half-time break at the State of Origin match in Sydney in 2003. A chance to make a few quick notes before finding out what both teams' coaches had to say to their respective sides. Origin games are a great adrenalin rush – even for broadcasters!

As a kid growing up in Singleton, NSW, there was only one hero for me: fast bowler Dennis Lillee. Getting to meet Dennis, have lunch with him and interview him at an Excalibur Club function in Newcastle was a great thrill. I have no doubt he has inspired many cricketers to push that little bit harder. Sometimes you meet your heroes and walk away disappointed – I didn't!

Pat Rafter, one of the nicest blokes you'd ever want to meet and a true champion in every sense. I met Pat when he was in Newcastle to help raise money for the region's Rescue Helicopter Service in 2003.

At the most critical moment in my life, close friends Chris Williams and Kathy Stewart were there to get me through and get me the help I so desperately needed. This picture of Chris and Kathy was taken at my fortieth birthday party in January 2003.

60 Minutes reporter Peter Overton (left), Chris Williams (right) and I retrace my steps along the platform at Broadmeadow railway station during taping of 'Out of the Darkness', a story *60 Minutes* presented on depression in early 2004. Things were a heck of a lot worse four years earlier when Chris and I were last together at Broadmeadow.

The forum was a very successful and powerful event attended by mental health professionals, psychiatrists and psychologists as well as families suffering the fallout of suicide and others crying out for help. After the speeches had concluded and the gathering was breaking up into smaller knots for discussion, I noticed a very attractive girl in her mid to late teens making her way towards me. Her eyes were raw from weeping, her cheeks stained with tears. With a monumental effort to control her emotions she told me that she had come along that evening to thank me. Her dad was the caller who had spoken to Diana. It had been a breakthrough moment in his suffering. After hanging up, he had taken Diana's advice. For the first time he had turned to his family and related to them exactly what he had been going through. As his loved ones they had rallied around him and now they were getting help. Chance is a fine thing. Had we not been on air talking about the subject or had her dad not tuned in at that time, what might have befallen him and his family? From that moment on I have remained totally convinced that my decision to be a public advocate for mental health awareness is the right one.

It comes as no surprise to note that depression and other forms of mental disorder are on the rise. As a society we have created a highly pressured environment that throws up a myriad of stressors to trigger the onset of breakdown. We're letting our kids loose in this dog-eat-dog world with the message that they had better perform or else. The professionals will tell you that the onset of many mental disorders occurs most frequently in the late teens or early

ARE THERE DIFFERENT TYPES OF BIPOLAR DISORDER?

There are two main types of the disorder. Bipolar disorder type I is distinguished by one or more manic episodes or mixed episodes and often one or more major depressive episodes. A depressive episode may last for several weeks or months, alternating with intense symptoms of mania that may last just as long. Between episodes, there may be periods of stability. The highs can be very intense, accompanied by lack of sleep, hallucinations, increased libido, psychosis and grandiose delusions – like thinking you are Jesus Christ.

Bipolar disorder type II usually entails one or more major depressive episodes accompanied by at least one hypomanic episode. Hypomanic episodes have symptoms similar to manic episodes but are less severe. Between episodes, there may be periods of stability. Because bipolar II is more subtle than bipolar I it can take longer to identify and diagnose.

Cyclothymic disorder is a milder form of bipolar disorder in which the periods of both depressive and hypomanic symptoms are shorter, less severe, and do not occur with regularity. It is distinguished by chronic fluctuating mood disturbance involving periods of hypomania and depressive symptoms. Many, but not all, people with cyclothymic disorder may develop a more severe form of bipolar disorder.

When someone experiences the symptoms of a manic episode and a major depressive episode, but does not fit into the above types of bipolar disorder, the condition is known as Bipolar Disorder Not Otherwise Specified. As with the other types of bipolar, it is a treatable disorder.

twenties. What's happening to a young person in that time-frame of, say, seventeen to twenty-three? He or she is under pressure to study hard, compete and get a good pass in the Higher School Certificate to win admission to university which, while perhaps producing a degree, will run up a serious HECS debt. The message is: you'd better do very well or you haven't got a hope in life. In the same period this young person would be coming to grips with great hormonal change, stepping out of their comfort zone into adulthood, serious relationships, the prospect of leaving home for the first time, plotting a career path and wondering how to fund a roof over their head when home afford-ability is out of reach and job security is a luxury of the past. Given that bill of goods, we shouldn't be asking ourselves *why* kids are doing drugs. You weigh up those pressures and say *why not?*

Many folk have a predisposition to mental disorder but can happily get through their lives without major incident. In other words, they don't encounter a trigger or stressor big enough to precipitate an episode. A kid graduates through the relatively stress-free years of early childhood to adolescence. Then – *wham* – in his or her late teens, and in a very confined passage of time, that kid is absolutely bom-barded with enough triggers to set off World War III. Little wonder that when young people present with a mental disorder the physician asks, 'What sort of drugs are you on?' Kids are looking for space from these pressures and instead of affording them that space, we keep putting the pressures back in their faces. Every other news bulletin carries the subliminal message that the society they are entering is riddled with danger, stress and the absence of opportunity.

Just before this book was due to go to the publisher, Louise answered our front door to a man who was in a state of distress. He was looking for me to talk to his 20-year-old daughter, who he was afraid was on the verge of suicide. She had an apparently terrific media job in Sydney and was bright and popular with her friends. But, to the dismay of her family, her world had turned black. When I learned of their plight, I visited the family home and spoke with the daughter, telling her of my own experiences and how I had found help. As a family they would still have a long way to go, but at least they had a place to start. The look of relief on the dad's face when I bid farewell said it all.

Growing up in regional Australia where I was an average student, I never encountered those sorts of pressures. My life was about playing sport, mixing with my mates, having a good time and generally leading a blissful existence. I never stressed about my Higher School Certificate results or career prospects. Was I wrong? I don't think so. By loading our kids up with a win-at-all-costs, sink-or-swim value system, we are setting them up for disaster. The pressure to compete in what is now a global environment is causing so many of our societal ills. It wasn't until later in life, when my career and family existence became overloaded with commitments, that my problems kicked in.

That manifesto of pressures is very difficult for women; but for one reason or another, it is particularly hard on men.

As boys we were groomed to be breadwinners, to have a career which defined our entire existence and place in society. We never hear a man described as a father and a good bloke. No, what defines him is how he generates money: coalminer, lawyer, salesman. The statistics indicate women want to marry men with good career prospects. Now, men find themselves trying to compete in a global market where there is no such thing as job security. Constantly, they are required to meet performance indicators that pay no heed to illness, caring for children, personal health and well-being. There is no safety net. The prospect of being cast on the career scrapheap in your forties with no chance of discharging the mortgage, financing your children's education, or maybe even saving your marriage, is all too real and the examples all too abundant. Rather than look at this situation and recognise how unworkable it has become, we take the pressures home and dump them on our families. Instead of rectifying the program, bureaucrats endorse it by tuning education and training to respond to these absurd demands. It is great to achieve, but when we have created an environment which pushes people beyond their limits, we are inviting disaster.

As a society we sit in the middle of this growing mess, scratching our heads about youth suicide, youth drug abuse, family breakdown, why young people are presenting with mental disorders in such numbers, why single dads are taking their own lives. Meanwhile, our leaders continue to treat the drug problem as a criminal rather than a community health issue. They can't see the wood for the trees.

WHAT EFFECTS CAN BIPOLAR HAVE?

Those of us who have been diagnosed with bipolar have grown to learn some of the simple truths associated with the illness. For instance, when psychiatrists refer to a major mood disorder they are talking about an imbalance in the mood-regulating system of the brain. In most cases, bipolar is a lifelong condition. As my household found, it is not easy living with a manic depressive. The suffering it causes can present devastating complications including marital breakdown, job loss, alcohol and drug abuse, and suicide. Those in strong partnerships or marriages are better able to cope with their depressive episodes. UK research has suggested that the divorce or separation rate is as high as 60 percent. Perhaps more alarming is that 25–50 percent will make one attempt at suicide. Of these, 10–15 percent will succeed. The risk is highest in the initial years of the illness. But, the good news is that these awful outcomes can be avoided with accurate diagnosis and proper treatment of the illness.

Prohibition has never worked. Instead, we should be asking the question: why do people need to do drugs, why do they need to drink alcohol to excess? The answer: to get themselves out of a reality that no longer works for them. All alcohol and drugs do is mask the problem. Of course, as tolerance increases, you need ever larger amounts of drugs or booze to build a bigger mask. But the problem remains.

If we examine why people need to get out of it, then we can start moving towards the whole issue of happiness and mental well-being. By continuing to deny that these problems exist, as a society we have no hope of creating positive change. We have to look at it differently.

Marijuana was readily available during my late teens. I tried it, smoked a few joints and pulled a few bongs. But the effect was lost on me. I didn't enjoy it. Today's hydroponically grown dope is so much stronger and the weight of evidence about the relationship between long-term use and the onset of mental disorder continues to grow.

From time to time I bump into one of the nurses who cared for me at James Fletcher. He is a very compassionate individual and always asks after my welfare. The last time we spoke I was able to tell him how well things were going and that with the help of medication and yoga, I was managing my life. He said, 'You've got three things going for you: one, you are of above average intelligence; two, you've got a good insight into the illness; and three, you don't smoke pot.'

'Really?' I responded.

'If kids weren't smoking the pot that's around today, I'd be out of a job.' And he went on to say how many people he sees presenting with a drug-induced psychosis who go on to be diagnosed as having bipolar, schizophrenia, depression or some other disorder. They have tried smoking dope thinking that it is relatively benign and socially acceptable – definitely not one of the big ticket items like cocaine, speed or heroin. But for those individuals with a predisposition,

WHO GETS BIPOLAR, AND WHY?

Research indicates that about 1–2 percent of the population has a bipolar disorder. It doesn't discriminate – men and women are equally likely to be affected. Bipolar is often associated with creative and productive people of a higher than average socio-economic status. Many of these achievers recognise the symptoms and ride the highs to success. Most people diagnosed with bipolar are in their teens or early twenties, although it can sometimes start in early childhood or as late as the forties or fifties. The majority have experienced drug or alcohol abuse at some point in their lifetime. The experts talk about a genetic predisposition to bipolar mood disorder. In other words, it's been imprinted on our circuitry since before we were born, waiting for an event to trigger an episode. Environmental factors such as stress and loss plus anything that impacts on the mood control areas of the brain may trigger it. For anyone diagnosed with bipolar disorder it is important to understand that it is not your fault. This is not an illness of guilt or a by-product of a weak personality. Nor is it an infection or a disease which can be contracted through contact with others. Simply, it stems from the genetic map drawn for us when we were still in the womb. Like so many of life's surprises, it can lie dormant for years, waiting to spring an ambush. Yes, it may hang around for life, but proper treatment can make all the difference.

smoking pot is the lighting of the wick. Don't take my advice on this; go and talk to mental health experts and they will tell you they see it every day.

My growing conviction that we've been missing the bleeding obvious about mental health was further consolidated by a recent report highlighting the ignorance and misconceptions surrounding my particular illness. It provided a snapshot of the true cost of mismanaging this problem. The report, *Bipolar disorder: Costs: An analysis of the burden of bipolar disorder and related suicide in Australia*, revealed that people with bipolar disorder are often misdiagnosed and left untreated, causing unnecessary suffering and costing the community millions of dollars. Commissioned by SANE Australia, a national charity promoting awareness, education and research into mental health, the report highlighted the need for early and urgent intervention on behalf of those suffering bipolar disorder. It cited knock-on effects which impact not just on the sufferer but on their family and the broader community.

Up to sixty percent of people with bipolar disorder have a substance abuse problem and the divorce rate is double the national average. Worse still, the suicide rate is twelve times the national average – one in six Australians with bipolar disorder takes his or her own life. On one hand, community awareness of depression and schizophrenia has improved, yet bipolar disorder, while as common as schizophrenia, remains under-recognised. A third of Australians with the disorder do not receive any treatment and the majority of the remainder receive inadequate treatment.

The more I read about the illness, the more it became apparent that here was a significant sector of the community suffering in near anonymity. It strengthened my resolve to speak out and make a contribution, no matter how humble, to raising awareness. The good news for me and all my fellow bipolar sufferers out there is that we are in some pretty impressive company. In recent times the list of famous people brave enough to declare publicly that they have bipolar has grown. By putting their names to the illness they are not only helping to destigmatise the subject but, hopefully, encouraging fellow sufferers and their families to seek the help they need. The late Spike Milligan, Victorian politician and playwright Neil Cole, singer Peter Gabriel, actor Patty Duke, writer Penelope Rowe, country star Charley Pride, former Guns 'n' Roses frontman Axl Rose, CNN founder Ted Turner and Olympic swimmer John Konrads are on the list. From the pages of history you can nominate Winston Churchill atop a roll of extraordinary achievers whose behaviour suggested they too experienced the extremes of bipolar disorder.

13

THE HOUSE OF MIRRORS

We live in an era of instant gratification. Press a button, throw a switch, take a pill and you are where you want to be. The truth is, nothing is ever that simple. In spite of the wisdom of the ages about patience and the virtue of time, we have conned ourselves into believing we know better. It took a truckload of medication to haul me down from the Matterhorn of mania scaled on my way to 12 September 2000, but it would take insight and a series of major lifestyle adjustments to put my existence back on track.

Months after the event, I kept my fortnightly appointment with Dr Weiss, confident at the time that rest, relaxation, exercise, improved diet and the daily medication had just about levelled me out onto a plateau of well-being, wiser for the experience. I'm a poor judge. Dr Weiss would later tell me that during the consultation he was observing a patient who was still slightly elevated. He backed the opinion of his professional colleagues by reiterating the bipolar diagnosis. Despite the fact that I was still circumspect about this assessment, I appreciated Dr Weiss's manner and felt we had struck an early rapport.

Acceptance of my illness for what it was aided recovery. With acceptance came the impression that sanity was returning and with it a clearer vision of my condition and the forces which governed it. This process of soul searching had me asking the question: what has this all been about? It had taken eighteen months for this enormous process of flux to pass through my life. Why? Where did it come from? Was I to blame for it? Could I have prevented it?

Understanding a little of the science was important. It was a chemical condition in the brain which affected the brain's transmitters. That helped me appreciate the importance of medication in maintaining the brain's chemical balance. But that was only part of the puzzle. Gradually, I began to recognise that oversimplifying mental illness could be a trap in itself. By stripping it down to the simple equation of taking a pill to counteract a chemical imbalance I ran the risk of missing the major components that would aid my recovery.

Lifestyle matters enormously. The way you live, eat, what you drink, how you work, play and relax, what and how you think, how you react to stress are all important.

I laid these issues out on the table of my consciousness and went through them very carefully. In so doing, I began to see a clearer picture of myself: how I lived and interacted with the world around me; what sort of life I had been leading in the years before the breakdown. It also started to give me a glimpse of what was really important in my life and what sort of behaviours were worth jettisoning or, better still, not taking aboard in the first place. Those binge sessions on the grog were mulled over and I recognised that they had occurred when I was powering along in the upper levels of the mania. That binge drinking could not have been helpful, I thought. It can't have been a good lifestyle choice. So, I made a commitment to never revive that monster.

As I continued to work my way through this process, like a technician opening up a computer, it gave me a view of just how Craig Hamilton was wired. This perception generated a thought which amazes me still: I had lived for thirty-seven years on this planet and never given a single thought to what made me tick. Why is that? Why do we accept the tools we've been given for life and then forge on with the project of education, career, family and whatever, never stopping for an instant to run a specifications check on our own systems? Many of us can sail through life in this way seemingly content with our lot. But when a crisis swoops out of the blue to jeopardise everything we hold precious, we're obliged to rake through the coals of our existence looking for truth and meaning.

My recovery had actually started before the breakdown.

It sounds absurd, but it's true. Suffering depression and still some months away from hospitalisation, I had started helping myself. In the search for keys to unlock the black cell I had turned to natural remedies. My view was that they could do me no harm and might provide some relief from the torment. Years before, the rigours of a sporting life had swayed me on the therapeutic powers of a regular massage. During the 1980s lower back spasms from bowling or the twinge of a damaged hamstring had me wearing a path to the door of massage therapist Lee Clements. Throughout the winter of 2000, when my world was tumbling into a chasm of depression, weekly I'd haul my sad carcass to Lee's rooms in search of respite. She was familiar with the symptoms of exhaustion and there is no doubt her curative touch provided a spark of energy when the batteries seemed totally depleted.

During one such session Lee asked if I had ever considered trying yoga. Yes, I had thought about yoga – for all of three seconds – and, being an impatient, hyperactive individual, had dismissed it as too slow and boring to offer me anything. But, this time, the message was different. They say you don't find yoga, it finds you – when you are ready. And find me it did – exhausted, out of answers, at the end of my rope and in desperate search of salvation. If yoga looked like a lifeline, then the drowning man was going to grab it and hang on tight.

Merewether Public School, midweek, a bunch of mums and me – my introduction to yoga. Here, my sporting career was of little use. After the pounding from working down the pit and bowling countless overs, my back was as supple as a rusty girder. The wear and tear on my joints had left me with the flexibility of the Tin Man. Yoga was difficult but I was determined to stick at it. My tip for anyone starting yoga is to stay with it for about six or seven sessions and then make a decision whether you wish to continue or not. For the first five or so evenings I found it very difficult to hold the poses, but by the sixth it became gently apparent that a change was occurring. The concentration required to hold the poses took up an increasingly larger piece of my thought processes. The realisation was that during the two-hour yoga session, there was little room left for the meteor showers of negative thoughts which had been dominating my thinking throughout my depression.

Anyone suffering a major depressive episode has a whole jumbo load of baggage whirling around in his or her head. Yoga cleared the terminal. In trying to explain the good yoga had done me I told a friend it was like having a hundred emails in your inbox. By the end of the session they were all processed and deleted, leaving the mind clear and refreshed. The research is voluminous on the benefits of yoga for mind, body and soul. I still practise it today.

Another lifestyle change instigated by depression was the decision to knock off the grog. It wasn't a difficult call. In that state the last thing you want to do is party or socialise. Later, I would learn that my drinking days were more a by-product of the elevated phases when I was hyperactive and wanted to party. Quitting the booze when I was in the grip of depression was no imposition. Rather,

I wanted to give my mind and body a chance. With a regime that included regular massage and yoga, it would have been crazy to ingest anything that made me feel any worse. Instead, my beverage of choice became herbal tea. The antioxidants of green tea were considered helpful as were the calming effects of camomile. A different form of relief from the pain and fatigue of depression was found in long hot baths augmented with aromatherapy oils.

None of these therapies provided anything remotely like a definitive cure for my depression. But they did soothe, enliven, relax and encourage me at a time when I was dangerously close to believing there was absolutely no way forward. Right now, you might be asking yourself: but what good were these therapies in the light of Craig's awful breakdown of September 2000? None of these so-called remedies were any help then, were they?

No, you are absolutely right. Nothing on the face of this Earth was going to stand in the way of that avalanche. But, on my release from hospital and after grudgingly admitting that the psychiatrists were right and I was wrong about the bipolar disorder diagnosis, I resolved to do all within my power to restore normality to my life. In the weeks surrounding the psychotic episode, I had abandoned any sense of stable routine, including the massage and yoga. In an elevated mood you think you are invincible. But, sitting at home, picking through the rubble of a shattered existence, I recognised that those therapeutic practices observed during the depressive phase represented a useful foundation on which to rebuild.

It might sound a bit paradoxical, but the crash affirmed the need to return to my therapeutic regimen of massage and yoga. Picking up the traces I realised that many of the lifestyle choices I had made over the years were unhealthy and even self-destructive. My stroll through the house of mirrors had revealed that I definitely had an illness and would be an absolute fool if I did anything more to make it worse. Throughout my convalescence and tentative return to work, I felt fragile and that sense of vulnerability further committed me to the concept of being kind to myself. The message was clear: don't create any bad situations for yourself, choose wisely and refuse to be a victim. Call it raised consciousness if you like, but a voice deep inside of me was saying: 'You can manage this by looking at the choices and decisions you have made and sorting the good from the bad.' Had my breakdown not occurred, I'm certain I would have gone along merrily repeating the same mistakes, making poor life choices and suffering the consequences. That's why my crash had to happen. Otherwise, I would never have heeded the lessons.

So, I picked up all those elements again – yoga, massage, the herbal teas and relaxation techniques. On walking back into that yoga class for the first time after my breakdown, it was heartening to see the familiar faces. I suspect most knew some of the detail of what had befallen me and why I hadn't been around for a few months. But there was no judgement or pity in their greetings. People who have been around yoga for a while understand how it opens up your feelings and perceptions, stripping away bias and baggage.

Yoga has an impressive track record in helping people who have encountered trauma, notably Vietnam veterans suffering post traumatic stress syndrome. As a pilgrim who had experienced suffering, yoga offered me sanctuary.

At first I was a bit rusty, but after three weeks or so the benefits started to come flooding back. I found that the techniques for breathing and meditation were eminently portable; I could take them anywhere and practise them often. In that first uncertain year back at work, whenever there was a deadline to meet or difficult task to perform, it was such a comfort to be able to alleviate the stress with a few minutes of breathing and meditation. The singular impact was invigorating and the accumulative effect divinely profound. In its gentle way this process calmed the mind, refurbished my damaged soul, cleared my vision and gave me the impetus to move forward once again. The process of yoga and meditation offered welcome stopping points in an otherwise busy day to listen to the self.

In my frenetic existence I had never paused for a moment to clear my mind and pay heed to the sounds of silence. I didn't have a spare five minutes for unnecessary mumbo-jumbo like meditation. I was driven; and when you are driven you just keep on forging ahead at the whim of the ego in a relentless hurry to get somewhere fast. No room, no time for introspection. Exhausted? Of course I was exhausted, I'd been running like a mouse on a treadmill for all of my adult life. Meditation taught me that my priorities were totally upside down. In meditation I found thoughts would drift in and out like tissues on a breeze and by calmly letting them go, the space between these thoughts became longer. In time those intervals identified themselves as the meditative space. In these quiet interludes lay peace and insight. At times I would kid myself that I was too tired or busy to go to yoga; but once there I'd realise again just how beneficial and important the weekly sessions had become to my improving sense of calm and well-being.

The process of rebuilding my life revealed that many of the things I had held to be true were constructed on a foundation of sand. Massive adjustment would have to be made. Without yoga and meditation I'm certain the first year after the breakdown would have been a great deal more difficult to manage. For much of it, I was very tired. Physically and mentally my entire being had encountered extremes nobody could imagine. It was as if every fibre had been zapped and scorched by a Chernobyl-scale meltdown and those still operating could only manage minimum voltage. The healing peace of yoga and meditation gave this traumatised system a chance to recover.

My former self was an adrenalin junkie, a six-cups-of-coffee-a-day maniac. Caffeine was the drug of choice – legal, affordable and, in sufficient quantities, bound to have me speeding like an over-amped lab rat. Coffee provided the jumper leads for getting me up and alert to call the football. The schedule for one particular weekend had me on air in Newcastle at six o'clock for the breakfast show, finishing at ten, jumping in the car for the two-hour drive to Sydney where I caught a flight to Auckland, had just enough time to drop my gear at a hotel before heading to the ground for the match broadcast. Then it was straight back to the hotel for a couple of quick beers, off to bed to wake on Sunday morning at 3 am Sydney time, catch a direct flight to Melbourne to be on air at noon, fly back to Sydney on Sunday evening, jump in the car for the return leg to Newcastle, fall into bed about midnight to be up in time to deliver the footy wrap on air at eight-thirty on the Monday morning. Imagine how much coffee would be imbibed to power me through that program. Already wound up to hyperactive overload, for me, coffee was hardly the right stimulant. Instead of an upper, I should have been drawing my energy banks from better quality rest and relaxation. Without proper rest and a chance to naturally recharge the batteries, the instinct to run constantly on adrenalin can be very dangerous. Twice the light in half the time.

The yoga and meditation gave me a calmer foundation from which to observe my life and events surrounding it. For relaxation, I read – not purely as a form of escape but a means to increase self-knowledge and discover ways to improve my well-being. A book by a former business executive detailed how at fifty-five he had burnt himself out on a diet of coffee, cigarettes and a remorseless program of chasing his corporate goals until he was diagnosed with cancer and the early signs of heart disease. He related how he had crashed, totally reassessed his lifestyle and abandoned the corporate rat race for a better quality of life. He talked about the power of diet and, in particular, fruit and vegetable juices. I bought a juicer and bega... his recipes for the various combinations of apple, ora... ginger, celery, carrot and beetroot. Some of them looked hideous, but they tasted beautiful and provided a great vitamin- and mineral-rich start to every day.

I became further convinced when I spotted a book by one of my cricket heroes, Greg Chappell. This publication didn't tell me how to take a slips catch or execute a cover drive; it was purely about the health benefits of good diet and strongly advocated the values of juices. I thought, if it is good enough for Greg Chappell, then I'm going to give it a go. Now, I'm onto watermelon, pineapple, orange and ginger at about 10.30 am instead of a coffee; and, of an afternoon around three, it's a carrot, celery, apple, ginger and beetroot detox. They are almost like another meal, which means I don't need so much food.

Eating more sensibly had additional benefits. My cholesterol levels had tended to run too high, so it was an even smarter choice to cut back on animal fats for more fruit and vegies, plenty of leafy greens and fish. As a result I dropped from 92 kilograms to my ideal weight of about eighty-six. What a difference! Moderation is a wonderful thing and gives me the excuse to still enjoy a block of chocolate and the occasional packet of chips. The practice of running on empty is something I'd never wish to repeat. As an added insurance to compensate for anything that my diet might be lacking, I take a B complex vitamin tablet daily. My approach is to give body and mind every chance.

In addition to the more obvious physical benefits, there

is something very therapeutic about knowing that you are being kind to your body, purging it of the toxins and flushing goodness through every cell and fibre. At long last I paid heed to the accepted wisdom that we don't drink enough water. At the same time, I cut right back on alcohol to the point where light beer became my social drink of choice. Only occasionally would I have a full-strength beer and, since 2000, I have averaged no more than two bourbon and Cokes a year. Don't get me wrong – I'm no gospeller for the evils of alcohol. My decision to cut it back was simply a choice for me, nobody else.

These choices weren't foisted upon me by a physician. Rather, I made them on my own. With those positive choices came a sense of personal empowerment that slowly rolled back the awful feeling of vulnerability I had experienced since my release from hospital. With a proper fluid intake, the vitamin-rich drinks and a more careful adherence to a healthy diet, my physical health rapidly improved.

Reading also offered me valuable insights from the wisdom of others. Before the breakdown, my reading had been restricted to biographies and sporting publications. Through my convalescence I realised additional tools would be needed to enhance my recovery. Achieving this end meant fast-tracking the process of acquiring more wisdom. Books provided the greatest access to both. My reading list included *Autobiography of a Yogi* by the great Indian spiritualist Paramhansa Yogananda, a hefty tome handed on to me by Paul Harragon, who gave it a high recommendation. It wasn't an easy read but it contained great messages about

empowerment and the choices we can make to
our lives.

From there I moved on to the writings of the Dalai
Lama, *The Tibetan Book of Living and Dying* by Sogyal
Rinpoche, *The Alchemist* by Paulo Coelho, and any number
of publications which might fit into the self-help category.
Some of the content tapped into my consciousness and I
was able to take a little out of each to deposit in my bank
of self-knowledge. Reading stimulated and opened up my
mind, forcing me to think about the options available to
us to improve our existence. The overarching message was
that we all have the power to heal ourselves providing we
can acquire the tools. Our thoughts are very powerful; in
fact, they shape us. When we are so ill that we have become
extremely depressed, our thoughts can not only take us
there, but they can keep us there by a constant cycle of
negativity. And once you are in that cycle, it is very hard
to break.

One negative thought spins into the next, creating a
domino effect of unrelenting negativity, a chain reaction
that goes on and on. Unless you have a circuit breaker you
have no idea how low it will take you. It forces you to a dark
place where there are no defining boundaries. You can
imagine yourself in the impenetrable dark, extending your
arms to try and identify some dimension, but you can't
touch the walls. They could be a few centimetres away or a
million miles. You can't see or sense the limits. How much
more suffering is there? Lost, blind in this dark place of
which you can make no sense, you simply despair. And that

despair can lead to suicide. I have been to that place and never want to go there again. Hence my desire to acquire the tools and the capabilities to make the right lifestyle choices which will give me the best fighting chance of living my life in the light.

I tell myself and anyone who is interested that my breakdown is the best thing that ever happened to me. As torturous and traumatic as it was, it has given me an insight I never would have gained had I not been compelled to enter the hall of mirrors and take a good old-fashioned look at myself from all angles. As the saying goes: a life unexamined is a life not worth living.

This insight would have been worthless had I chosen not to act on it. An early test came at the ABC Christmas party of 2000. In previous years the party would have been over at midnight, but a core of revellers would move on to the next venue. That party would run its course and then a subset of survivors would move on to a nightclub. No matter how many subsets were left standing, I would always be there to the death. Midway through the evening of the 2000 Christmas bash, I sensed that old feeling – I knew where this one was heading and realised I no longer wanted to go down that road. I stopped drinking at about eleven-thirty and for the next hour or so simply enjoyed the company of my colleagues at a special time of the year before contentedly catching a cab home. The compulsion to invent another party to kick on to and keep the night rolling towards a binge session had been conquered.

Short-term commitment is fine, but could my resolve

stand the test of time? A typical test came three or so years after my breakdown when the work crew booked a ferry cruise on Lake Macquarie as the backdrop for a great social evening. Once upon a time, such an event would have prompted the old me to cast off all inhibitions and drag the binge-drinking party animal out of the closet. But at a reasonable hour I found myself once again sharing a cab ride home with friends. I don't miss the marathon party life one bit; nor do Louise and the kids.

One of the great gifts of the post-breakdown period was that I finally grew to appreciate the value of rest and relaxation – *that wonderful state of just doing nothing*. I can now go away on a holiday, lie on a banana chair with a book and relax. And I am happy to do that all day. The need to belt off down the beach for a training run, cycle up a mountain or simply be on the go for no other reason than being on the go has at long last left me. Today, when I'm lying back in this relaxed mood it occurs to me that my former inability to sit still must have driven Louise and company crazy. In the past, I couldn't live any other way. Now, it is wonderful to just lie back and smell the roses. Work hard when you have to be productive, but take the quality down time and enjoy it.

Exercise will always be important to me, but in a moderated form. When it came to physical activity, the bloke I used to be was patently way over the top. These days I manage to keep myself in reasonable shape with touch football, swimming, lifting a few weights at home and going for a bike ride once a week. But I'm no longer throwing myself into two or three sessions a day. Instead, my exercise is relaxed and varies from having a romp in the surf with the kids to going for a stroll.

Rest, relaxation, diet, yoga, meditation and exercise are all part of the jigsaw of well-being. Another vital part of my jigsaw is medication. When you have a diagnosed illness such as bipolar disorder, your doctor will tell you how you can manage it by taking the prescribed medication. In my case it is Epilim, or sodium valporate, a medication used to control mania. As Dr Alan Weiss explained, it keeps the patient in the mid-range of moods. But bipolar is a tricky beast and it can fool you. There have been times since Epilim was first prescribed when I have said to myself: 'I'm travelling fine, I don't need this medication anymore. I'm okay.'

It's a trap. There is such a huge desire to throw away the crutch because, as humans, we want to believe that we have won this personal battle – beaten the illness. It's ego, the competitive side of human nature that wants to win. For the first year after the crash I was slowly getting better and recognised Epilim's role in that recovery. Six months later I was feeling so well that I started to question whether I still needed the medication. But I persevered, continuing to take my medicine and put my life back together. By the second half of 2003 I was feeling so well, so much on top again, that I began to hear an insidious voice whispering in my ear: 'Go on, you've beaten it, you don't need the Epilim. You're stronger than that.'

Without consulting my psychiatrist, I started backing

off the medication, reducing it from 1500 mg a day to a thousand. In other words, I had cut my daily intake from three 500 mg tablets down to two. I needed to know whether I was beating this demon. My self-analysis was that my mood was exactly where it needed to be. I was going okay. Yet, when I paid my next visit to Dr Weiss late in 2003 and told him that I had cut back on the medication, he noted that I was a little more up than I should have been. It was another tap on the shoulder to remind me just how subtle the illness can be in activating a rise in mood that you fail to notice. That's the trap. Just when you think you're going *real* well and are on top of things, you are actually going *too* well. Fortunately, I listened to Alan Weiss. His message was: 'Next year is an important time. You are going to produce a book on your experiences and the Olympics will be coming around again to remind you of what happened four years before. I want you medicated at the level I have prescribed for you.'

It was a timely reminder. Because of the horrendous outcomes, there is no room for complacency with this disorder. The crash of 2000 revealed in the worst possible way just who or what was driving the wagon that day and it certainly wasn't me. It was bipolar in all its towering horror. You can never put this awful genie back in the bottle – *but you can manage it*. Meanwhile, that small battle within me continues – a part of me still wants to declare victory over the illness while the other knows that I must maintain my medication.

In my particular case, there is another complication to

managing the illness. As I mentioned earlier in the book, I have volunteered myself as an advocate for mental health. In one sense, this role runs contrary to my personal recovery and management program. At a time when I had jettisoned a heap of external activities and learned the discipline of rest and relaxation, here I was taking on yet another commitment – and one about which I was very passionate. Not surprisingly, this set a few small alarm bells ringing in my psychiatrist's rooms. Like most professionals in his field, Dr Weiss is deeply committed to achieving more awareness of mental health, but there is a greater imperative: his responsibility to me as his patient. If I insisted on taking on this added role then I would have to learn to manage it and factor it in with all the other lifestyle adjustments made for my recuperation. And Dr Weiss would be watching closely.

With the active support of media colleagues like television journalists Melinda Smith, with whom I had collaborated on a 'We Care' community program, and Jim Callinan, I became emboldened by my efforts to publicise mental health. I was fiercely determined to do more but also angry that, right across the nation, we had been so slow to recognise and react to the issue. I had taken a public stance on depression and associated illnesses by featuring on a number of radio programs, organising a public forum and appearing on TV.

Early in 2004 I received a phone call from Richard Mortlock, a producer with the Nine Network's *60 Minutes* program. Richard explained that he and *60 Minutes* reporter

Peter Overton were working on a story about depression. A media contact had mentioned to Richard that a certain ABC sports broadcaster had experienced his share of problems. Richard had tracked me down to put the question: would I be interested in sharing my experiences with their TV audience? He explained that Peter would be filing a story that was very close to his home and heart. His mother-in-law Penelope Rowe, the author and mother of Peter's wife, Channel Ten newsreader Jessica Rowe, would be coming out with the details of her lifelong battle with bipolar. Given the intimacy and sensitivity of the issue, would I be willing to add my name and experiences as a supplement to Penelope's revelations?

At the time, I had started work on this book so my commitment to publicising depression and bipolar disorder was already underway. However, I realised I had an obligation to the publisher and didn't wish to do anything that would impinge on plans for the book. Also, as a media employee, I knew that constraints of time and space can make it difficult for even the most diligent reporters and producers to do justice to a story. In my view, this was a very important issue and I was wary about blowing what might be one of the very few chances to shed some wholesale light on the subject.

The *60 Minutes* opportunity was discussed with the publisher as well as family and confidants. Louise was very wary. Understandably, the pain associated with my breakdown was still very much a raw wound for my wife and family. Louise didn't need her medical training to know that you don't scratch a wound. My best mate and brother-in-law Scot Leighton, an uncomplicated bloke with no great respect for the media circus, was equally circumspect. Scotty knew that a story can take on a life of its own, leaving those most affected to manage the fallout. Both Louise and Scot were concerned about the sort of effect high exposure of such an intimate family experience would have on our kids.

Over the space of a few days I weighed up the pros and cons and ultimately decided I would accept the opportunity to appear on the program. I was swayed in part by the fact that in dealing with an issue close to his own family, Peter Overton would be supremely motivated to achieve the best outcomes for all concerned. As one of Australia's most-watched shows, the Sunday evening current affairs program offered a tremendous opportunity to illuminate what a number of experts, in reference to its low profile, describe as the forgotten psychiatric disorder.

It was impossible not to be impressed by Penny Rowe's story. The writer was part of that generation of Australians compelled by the constraints of the time to manage life's setbacks behind a façade of stoicism. Mental illness was rarely admitted, never discussed, hidden from view behind shuttered minds and drawn curtains. Penelope and her daughters had paid a dear price for her long battle with bipolar. Bravely, she gave her pain some ventilation in her 1997 novel *Blood Songs* (Minerva Fiction), a barely fictional account of a woman, not unlike Penelope Rowe, who suffers a debilitating breakdown. The *60 Minutes* story would be her, and her family's, ultimate disclosure. When I became aware of Penny's journey, it was difficult for me to turn my back without offering some form of support and solidarity.

My cause was aided by a contribution from Australian and Newcastle Knights rugby league captain Andrew Johns. During filming, the game's best player fronted the camera to deliver a heartfelt plea for better understanding of the issue.

The segment went to air in March 2004 and instigated a tremendous response among viewers. As I had come to learn via my own experiences and extensive reading on the subject, bipolar was indeed the forgotten mental illness. There was very little official awareness of bipolar. Not only was the *60 Minutes* mailbag crammed with responses about the need to demystify the illness, I personally received a number of letters from friends and associates expressing similar sentiments. Peter phoned me from Far North Queensland where he was on his next assignment to say that the reaction to the story had been massive. That sort of feedback convinced me that bipolar is way more prevalent than anybody had ever expected. At some stage in their lives, most people will experience some sort of mental trauma, anguish or setback. Why, when such events are so common, do we as a community continue to ignore mental illness and pretend it simply doesn't happen? There is no reason for there to be such a cloak of secrecy. We need to understand that mental illness is something which can touch each and every one of us – it is not confined to just a crazy few. We're all vulnerable.

No man is an island, though. Other people – Louise, the kids, friends and family – are touched by whatever happens to me. While I am forging on, keeping watch on my mood and helping with the publicity battle, I must be forever alert that those closest to me aren't cut down by friendly fire. To put it simply, outing myself about mental illness might do them some harm. I was pretty happy with the *60 Minutes* story but my mother didn't like it at all. The natural response of a mother is to nurture and protect and it would have been confronting to see a firstborn baring his soul, describing the most horrendous happenings on national television. Dad was okay, he understands how passionately I feel about the subject and is accepting of my position. Both my sister Kate and brother Ian gave me positive feedback about the story despite the risk of it having serious implications for them. After all, every time I lay myself bare on this subject, somebody they know knocks on their door and says, 'What about your brother – look what he's done now!'

After Dr Weiss provided a section on his insights for this book, he rang to say that he would like a debrief. My impression was that he wanted to talk about what he had submitted and whether I'd be happy about it appearing in black and white. Instead, when he spoke about his concerns for my health and that he hadn't liked what he had seen on *60 Minutes* – me in a very passionate, hyped-up state – you could have knocked me down with a feather. Again, it was another tap on the shoulder to remind me that the monster was still lurking close by. Dr Weiss said he was concerned that I appeared to be operating at a level above where he would prefer me to be. I conceded I was passionate and pumped, but pointed out that the editors had naturally selected the most compelling quotes from hours of filming and those grabs showed me in a fairly fervent light.

On reflection, I have to admit that the *60 Minutes* experience took a lot out of me. In the week before filming, I went into my cave and distanced myself from the family as I prepared in my mind how to approach a story that would hit so many people watching prime-time television. 'If we miss the mark here,' I said to myself, 'we'll set the cause back ten years.' When the filming was done, Louise and I went out to lunch with Richard Mortlock, Peter Overton and the crew and they could not have treated us more graciously. But, when we got home, Louise and I had a serious heart-to-heart. She broke down in tears and said: 'I can see things happening here that are so much like 2000. You are getting into that cave again, cutting yourself off from us. We don't know what's going on inside your head. You have focused so much on doing the *60 Minutes* piece properly that you haven't even been hearing me.'

I sat and listened without reply. Everything she said was absolutely correct and she needed to get it off her chest. My instincts had been not to worry Louise with the weight of expectation I had imposed on myself in preparing for the interview. But, because she knows me so well, she saw straight through it and was naturally worried enough to think, *here we go again*.

Thank God Louise told me what was on her mind because it certainly helped clear the air and restore perspective just when I needed it. We sat down as a family and watched the program. I don't think Louise enjoyed it. The kids thought it was novel seeing their dad on TV. As for me, I was on tenterhooks until the phone calls and emails starting coming in from people expressing how much the segment had meant to them. Putting the entire experience into the context of my recovery and continued management of my condition, it had taught me a major lesson: if I was going to be a worthwhile advocate for mental health awareness, I would have to learn how to manage the undertaking without placing my own well-being in harm's way. After all, what sort of champion for the cause would I be if I fell off my own horse?

14

'Hard for an Australian Male to Accept': Alan Weiss, Psychiatrist

I first met Craig on the eighteenth of February 2001 after he had been in James Fletcher Hospital the previous September. I understand he was preparing to go to the Olympics for the ABC, but never got there. In the referral note his GP wrote: 'Craig was treated for depression in the past year after a background of depressive episodes over the preceding few years. I understand that this manic episode he had when catching the train was his first.'

There are two major types of bipolar disorder: type I is where you have a severe mania very often associated with psychosis which inevitably leads to the sufferer being admitted to hospital. Psychosis can simply be defined as being out of touch with reality. By definition, if you've had an episode like that you've suffered bipolar disorder type I. With bipolar disorder type II you have a hypo-manic episode but never get full-blown mania and rarely have psychotic symptoms. But you have more regular depressive episodes. In bipolar disorder type II the highs are less severe and the depressions relatively more severe. In type I, the highs are very severe and the depressions can also be very severe. Bipolar disorder type I, which is what Craig suffered, is the worse of the two.

As far as his medication is concerned, the mainstay of treating bipolar is a mood stabiliser drug. A mood stabiliser treats the high and the low and maintains equilibrium in the middle. Not many drugs are very good at performing those three tasks. Epilim (sodium valporate) is a core mood stabiliser, relatively good at treating the high and not so good on the low, but okay at maintaining the equilibrium. The gold standard is lithium carbonate (Lithicarb), which has been around since 1959. It tends to have more side effects so we use Epilim. Over the last ten years, there have been a number of new mood stabilisers. Of note, there has been the increasing role of the atypical antipsychotics in this area. Drugs like olanzapine (Zyprexa) now have a large amount of evidence to demonstrate they are very effective mood stabilisers.

When I met Craig he had just turned thirty-eight and he told me about the episode of mania he experienced in September 2000 as well as a number of depressive swings over previous years. He talked about 1999 when he had felt depressed for much of that year. At the time he didn't quite understand what was going on but simply that he had a depressed mood, was experiencing a lot of negative thoughts, had lost his libido and was very lethargic. Other symptoms were loss of appetite, loss of weight, fatigue, inability to concentrate, short-term memory problems, and withdrawal from social contacts. All of those are core symptoms of a major depressive episode. He described periods of five or so weeks when a 'switch' would go off in his head when he went down and experienced mild to moderate and even severe symptoms, but what they weren't associated with was suicidal thinking. I think that that is why he never presented for help at those times.

By the time I saw Craig he'd had had his first manic episode whilst attempting to catch the train at Broadmeadow station. He then described a number of stressors typical to bipolar sufferers in the lead-up to the mania. Stressors are events or happenings, either positive or negative, that are linked to the onset of an illness or episode. For example, getting married is positive but can be a stressor which carries with it a certain amount of change. Likewise for buying a house. Such events can bring people unstuck. In Craig's case, being overcommitted at work was a stressor. The other obvious one was the Olympic Games. For a sports journalist, this is probably the biggest positive stressor that he could experience in his entire life. For all of us who were in Sydney sometime during the Games, it was an edifying, euphoric experience. It gave me an appreciation of why a sports journalist would have been so subject to this event and why it could have been such a powerful trigger for a manic episode. As one of the journalists assigned to cover this event, and because he had a great deal of work to complete prior to going to the Games, he was under enormous pressure. Apart from the Olympics, another great stressor was how hard he had worked to secure his job at the ABC. He was extremely thrilled and honoured to win that most sought-after position.

We then talked about how in February 2000 he was starting to get more overwhelmed with fatigue and tiredness. He found it difficult to concentrate, was becoming more and more lethargic and was therefore under pressure at work. This is typical of people with busy jobs. They cope with it until depression sets in and then they become inefficient. They experience self-doubt and start to check their work. I think that was happening to Craig: he became increasingly inefficient. As he reported it to me, in about June 2000 he was doing a shift at the ABC and he was so incapacitated that all he could do was lie on the floor. He then had a period of three weeks' leave, which may have superficially recharged his batteries but I actually wonder what was going on in his mind. At this time, his GP commenced Lovan (fluoxetine or prozac), a selective serotonin re-uptake inhibitor (SSRI) which is a very common antidepressant. Lovan is a drug I do not prescribe all that commonly, particularly in bipolar. It increases the pooling of serotonin in the synapses of the neurons by preventing its recycling. The theory behind depression is that there is a depletion of serotonin to those neurons. The difficulty with the SSRI and Lovan is that it tends to stay in the body's system for long periods. That is very good for people who are non-compliant about taking their medication, but very challenging if you find the drug is not working. In the setting of a bipolar illness it can cause switching from one state to another. I understand the drug was increased to 40 mg, which is two capsules a day. After about a month Craig said he began to feel a whole lot better. His sense of hopelessness began to settle along with his suicidal tendencies. But then he began to suffer anxiety. To this point he had been experiencing a unipolar depression, not bipolar disorder.

My understanding is that over the break from work, the Lovan kicked in and Craig started to feel more like his old self. He described a steady increase in his mood from that point on, which Craig described as his mind gradually clearing. It is my opinion that at this point Craig went into a hypomanic state, a less severe form of mania, months before he became manic. Hypomania is the state we normally witness in bipolar type II sufferers. Bipolar II victims can go through a hypomanic period before hitting mania, but that is not always the case. There is this notion of 'switching' whereby they can go to bed at night and a 'switch' in their head turns on or off, taking them from one extreme to the other, hence the name bipolar. I do not think this happened to Craig; instead his switching happened gradually over a period of the next few months, culminating in the Olympics.

People were obviously concerned about him but, as he is a naturally exuberant person and because many of us were getting rather excited close to the Olympics, it was easy to explain away his high spirits. But then he started developing psychosis. For Craig, this occurred very close to the day he went to Broadmeadow station. In this same period he decided to appear on a radio talkback program about depression. This represented Craig's desire to tell the world what was happening to him. I suspected he could only do that if he was in a hypomanic or manic state, whereas if he had been depressed he would have cut himself off from such contact. He has since agreed that, with the benefit of hindsight, he was hypomanic. He was increasingly elated about going to the Games as a reporter. He described an elevated mood and that he was 'touched by God'. He had a religious experience and felt that he had come back to Earth as Jesus Christ. His mission was to go the Olympic Games and send a message of peace, harmony and goodwill to the world.

Initially, he did not share this plan with anyone else and superficially remained in control. It was only when he was compelled to go to the Olympics, via Broadmeadow station, under the command of God, that he 'lost the plot'. That was when he became heavily influenced by his delusional beliefs about Christ and God.

The discharge summary from James Fletcher dated 26 September noted that he had increased energy, decreased need for sleep, increased irritability and was heavily influenced by grandiose delusions. His thought disorder led him to believe he was dead and in heaven at the same time. This is so typical of someone with a bipolar disorder under the influence of a psychosis. What starts out as an elevated mood becomes increasingly intense; they usually have very pressured speech, talk very rapidly and have what we call 'flight of ideas'. That is, they understand what is happening but because their mind is going so fast, what you and I would hear is an absolutely intense rush of ideas all loosely fitting together with no semblance of normality.

Unlike many other sufferers of this condition, Craig wasn't using alcohol or other substances in a way that would contribute to his illness. Some sufferers do use alcohol, as a way of self-medicating. As for his binge drinking, that most likely occurred when he was in an elevated mood. His drinking was most likely a pattern based on his mood.

His discharge summary shows that he was admitted to James Fletcher, where he spent three days in intensive care under an involuntary order. That is pretty typical of the process in which a person with mania winds up getting help. They have lost sight of reality and entered the delusional stage. Craig now acknowledges that had we spoken to him in July or August 2000 there would have been no way we could have convinced him that events were starting to get out of control. He had just returned from depression and he thought that he was feeling his old self once again. People with bipolar actually believe that the high is their well state. We're not talking about the mania here but rather the hypomanic state.

If you take a grading of plus five and minus five as representing the two poles of bipolar disorder, then most sufferers view plus two as being a normal state. Ideally, their normal state should be zero, exactly midway between the two poles. In July and August 2000 Craig would have been operating at the plus two level and continuing to climb as he approached the Olympics. One of the biggest challenges for professionals treating this disorder is pegging the patient back to zero. It is a matter of helping them identify where they need to be rather than where they want to be. At first, they get quite despondent because they're accustomed to operating at the elevated level. Part of that despondency can be explained by the fact that many bipolar sufferers have been great achievers and have used their elevated state as a source of creativity. Look at what Craig achieved in working his way out of the mine to secure his dream career. They seem to have boundless energy and can survive on limited sleep, as Craig was doing in the weeks before the Games. He talked about some nights having five or six hours and others just two or three. He could burn the candle at both ends and be very productive – for a while.

Research has shown that bipolar is probably the most biological condition in psychiatry. Schizophrenia and bipolar disorder display the strongest evidence of a genetic link. I was at a conference recently when they were talking about the aetiology of bipolar disorder. It is of interest that they have now identified three alleles – part of the chromosome arms – as the most likely gene site associated with bipolar illness. It is in the genes and seems to run across all societies and all cultures. The caveat for that would be that people in higher socioeconomic groups have greater capacity to hide it. They tend to go to a retreat to get better.

They may run a big business and be very successful and take three weeks off when they get depressed. Because they may be very creative during the hypomania phase, people tend not to say anything. If you have five or six weeks of hyperactivity and then take a few weeks off, it doesn't matter because you've already achieved six months' work during that elevated period. However, that pattern tends to lead to burnout.

In a pre-industrial, agrarian time when people may not have been exposed to so many stressors or triggers, if you 'went a bit crazy, high or mad' it didn't matter so much. You may have run the sheep around the field at a rapid rate but the consequences of this act would not be as dramatic. Communities were much more tolerant. That tradition of small communities dealing with such issues still exists today in Third World countries. In Australia we may view ourselves as rugged individualists but I tend to think that is a way of masking our feelings. It is very hard for an Australian male to accept he may be suffering from depression.

How much is genetic and how much is environment? The triggers or stressors seem to be important in bringing out the underlying vulnerability to bipolar. We know that in patients with a severe bipolar type I illness, the stressors or triggers can be relatively mild. In their case a trigger could be drinking too much alcohol or smoking marijuana. The most common time for a patient to present for help is during the teenage years. Craig was an exception, which suggests that he didn't have the same vulnerability as some others.

When practitioners rate psychiatric illness they always

consider five axiom domains: Axis I is the psychiatric domain, Axis II is the personality or temperament domain, Axis III is any complicating physical illness, Axis IV is the stressor/triggers identified which we have discussed earlier, and Axis V is the level of the dysfunction that has occurred in the patient's life.

It is usual with most sufferers of mental illness to find a deterioration in the level of functioning over the twelve months prior to the onset of illness. In Craig's case, in the year preceding the Olympic Games we note the following areas of dysfunction: inability to manage work and reduced capacity to cope with home life. Initially this was due to depression but later was a result of hypomanic symptoms. That is a pretty classic scenario. It is not until you can help somebody to get better that they can look backwards on the process and start to identify what was happening to them.

It is very common for people suffering bipolar to present for treatment when they are suffering depression. Usually, that depression has not been preceded by a manic episode, except perhaps in the case where people have been using non-prescribed psychotropics or hallucinogenics. In its classic form bipolar is usually heralded by a depressive swing. And that's where you get caught because you treat unipolar disorder with antidepressants but they're the last thing you want to use for a bipolar sufferer because the patient will be switching. Antidepressants are known to increase the frequency and severity of the swings.

My impression is that Craig was always a 'livewire individual' but I do not believe his history of illness goes back beyond the ten years preceding his episode at Broadmeadow. Yet, personality can provide the access for the onset of illness. There was certainly a history of depression. But mostly he was a warm, exuberant guy. He would be the 'life of the party' even without the impact of the bipolar illness.

I do not believe that Craig has a personality disorder. A personality disorder is where a personality is deemed as being the primary cause or dynamic resulting in dysfunction or complicating a psychiatric illness.

If you analyse Craig's prominent personality features, he displays exuberance for life. He appears to have an internal locus of control representing a sense of narcissism. He loves to express himself. These features make him a good radio announcer.

It is difficult to really know whether there was or was not a component of his mood disorder in his early years. It could be that he was more exuberant at certain times when the impact of the mood disorder came into play. He led a very active sporting life with plenty of exercise and activity and I suspect that this could have masked the symptoms by burning off those energy levels. The fact that he has always been physically active and prided himself on exercise and looking after himself might explain why it was not evident at an earlier stage in his life.

From the time I started to see him, Craig has wanted to write a book. Initially, it was going to be about somebody else. But then it was about him. We eventually talked him out of it because it seemed like it represented a return of his manic symptoms. There is always a tendency to deny the illness. I believe that is part of being human. In fact, he was cutting down on his dosage of Epilim. What occurs is a loss of insight. So subtle are the hypomanic symptoms in the early stages that it is easy to be fooled. There is this extra dimension of grandiosity – an over-inflated sense of self – that needs to be looked for in the early phases.

I agree that seeing your 'shrink' is not the most agreeable thing to be doing, but when I recently suggested to Craig that I see him in three months' time he said, 'No, let's make it six.' I allowed him to make that call, but my reading of that behaviour is that he appeared 'slightly high'. I would like him 'running a bit lower'.

I didn't see the *60 Minutes* segment go to air but when I saw Craig immediately after it he looked quite flat. He actually described his change of character in the home environment during the build-up to him being interviewed for that program. I would have thought the interview would have been a fairly spontaneous sort of process, but Craig had gone into preparation mode for it days and days beforehand.

That's why I am wary about talking on the subject. I would like the world to know about bipolar illness; but I am also aware that with someone who has mania, you can play into his illness as a way of getting that message out there; and that will have a great consequence for him. In the case of the *60 Minutes* program, the viewer or audience may not be aware of his lack of insight. However, this is what we as professionals are trained to focus on, and it is my belief that insight is what is missing in Craig right now. It is of note that when he told me about preparing this book he had already agreed to appear on the *60 Minutes* program. I asked him about this and said 'Why didn't you tell me, as your doctor, about the *60 Minutes* program? Why did you tell me *after* the event?' Craig could not answer and made light of this question.

The other issue is non-compliance. By that we mean someone's refusal or inability to take treatment as prescribed. Treatment is not merely medication, it is following through with everything as prescribed. This includes changing lifestyle, relationships, looking after yourself, not drinking – all those things which in the ideal world would contribute to wellness. Not taking medication as prescribed is clearly an important area of non-compliance. Craig is at risk of being non-compliant because of his belief that he is doing everything possible to bring about balance and well-being in his life. However, at times when he is talking to me, I wonder what is fact and what is fiction. I say this as the impact of grandiosity can result in circumstances and events becoming elaborated in ways which change their reality. As a result, it is often not clear when a patient is becoming elevated. At these times, it is useful to take corroborative history from family and relatives. In conclusion, I am concerned that the process of non-compliance and some hypermanic symptoms may be playing into Craig's state at present. I was particularly concerned about this during my consultation in March 2004. Although he said that his mood was zero, I was concerned that he may be running at a plus two or three out of five.

I'll continue to see Craig as part of his ongoing care and am looking forward to checking his progress.

Alan Weiss BMBS (Flind.),
BSW (Hons) (UNSW),
FRANZCP
Cert. Accred. Child Psychiatry (RANZCP)
Consultant Psychiatrist

15

'Going Through a Bad Spell': Wayne Fowler, Cricket Mate

It might have been Peter Schacht who phoned me to say that he had heard from Louise and that Craig had been taken to James Fletcher. We agreed that we should go and see him as soon as possible. At first, he wasn't allowed any visitors but we managed to get in to see him after a few days. Peter came to my office in Bolton Street, which is just down the hill from the hospital. We drove up together. I was apprehensive about what sort of state Craig would be in. The story we had heard was that he had gone off the handle at the train station and that he had been restrained by police. Walking into a mental hospital under those circumstances you might find yourself wondering if the person you are about to encounter is the same bloke you have known for all these years. But somehow I knew that Craig would still be Craig. Yes, he's in trouble, I thought, but somehow he's going to get the help that he needs to bring him through.

It was pretty confronting to walk into what was basically a lock-down situation. The security was very intense. The medication Craig was on had caused a sort of lockjaw response. Fortunately for us, Craig explained that straight away by saying, 'When you look at me, I'm going to be making some stupid faces; but don't be alarmed, it's only a side effect of the medication.'

Nonetheless, I felt uncomfortable being there and seeing him in that condition. But, as our visit wore on and we continued to converse, it became apparent that Craig was still Craig. Our attitude towards him was to try and be as upbeat as possible. We asked him how long he anticipated being in hospital, how he was being treated and what sort of medication he was on. It was apparent he wasn't a hundred percent sure what was happening to him. He had recognised Peter and me when we walked in and seemed happy to see us. He even gave us a bit of a rundown on the other patients in his section. Although he was able to talk about the environment of which he was a part and wanted to get out of, he definitely knew he had a problem which had to be resolved. Then he said: 'One of the things which happened at the train station was that I thought I was Christ.' I wasn't sure what to make of that but simply took it at face value. By the time we saw him he knew he was Craig Hamilton, not Jesus Christ. But there were still parts of the picture he hadn't yet sorted out for himself.

By then he had understood his chances of going to the Games were gone. He realised that it would take a few weeks or months of treatment for his carers to really get to grips with his illness. I'm not sure whether he mentioned bipolar while we were there but he was definitely aware he was no longer going to the Games. It was very sad. Seven years or so before, when it had been announced that the Olympics would be held in Sydney, Craig had made it a huge career goal and had told all of us about his ambition to make it to the Olympics.

It's not an easy story. For example, when he first told his circle of close mates, one of them simply refused to believe that Craig, of all people, could have been suffering from depression. He just couldn't understand it.

For the first couple of years we had played against each other – Craig for Belmont and me for Charlestown. In 1985 we toured the UK together with the Cavaliers and struck up a friendship which has lasted. What was the basis? Common interests, I guess. We both loved cricket, enjoyed a good time, live music. Later, when our wives – Catherine and Louise – got to know each other they became firm friends. We started families at about the same time and our kids are roughly the same ages. We were both big fans of Midnight Oil and whenever the band was in town we would be there. The Oils were actually playing in London when we were on the Cavaliers tour. Unfortunately, Craig was doing something else that night but went along to see them. He wasn't happy about missing out.

When my cricket career finished in the mid-nineties we still kept in contact. With families on the way and our respective jobs – Craig in broadcasting and me in accountancy – we were both pretty busy but made a point of catching up for a barbecue or New Year's Eve and keeping in touch by phone. We all spent that millennium New Year's Eve together and I never noticed that Craig was feeling low. He's the sort of person who is always upbeat when he is talking to you, so nobody would have picked that he wasn't his usual self. No matter what was bothering him in life, he has always been the sort of person to say: 'Hey, I'm fine.'

I understand now that he had experienced some lows in the years before he admitted that he was suffering depression, but we never saw any sign of it. It might have been different for those living with him. We were all leading pretty hectic lives and had no real insight into it all. If we had caught up for, say, a game of tennis, he always had a joke, was always positive. He would say that he was busy but he would never admit that things might have been getting on top of him. He seemed so passionate about the broadcasting career, and it was evident he loved going away to Sydney and elsewhere with the football. It was clear he had really thrown himself into the job.

On top of that he was busy with trivia nights and speaking engagements. It was apparent he was working long hours. We were both at that stage of our lives when you're going at a hundred miles an hour without thinking about the consequences. You never stop and think that you might be doing yourself harm. It's a throwaway line: we always say to each other, 'How are you going?' and the answer is: 'I'm going fine.' If the truth of the matter is that you're feeling a bit weary, that work is getting on top of you, well, you don't admit it to your mates. Instead, we tend to say, 'Everything is going great, I'm loving the job and life is terrific.'

Thinking back through the years that I've known him, you'd never consider for a moment that a bloke like Craig would suffer from depression. Yet, it's amazing now the number of people you speak to and they will admit, 'Yeah, I had depression last year.' In any other circumstances, they wouldn't have mentioned it. Looking back, I can't think of one moment that would have given me a clue about what was going to happen to Craig. I had no idea what was happening to him during 1999 and 2000 until he phoned to say that he was going through a bad spell and needed a bit of time and space to get it sorted out. He said he had depression and that he wanted to be upfront with me so that I didn't hear it from someone else. Part of his plan was to cut back his workload because he was aware that he seemed to be having very few days off. Basically, he mentioned that he was seeing his doctor, getting the right help and reducing his commitments.

I think it was shortly after that when he phoned to say that he wanted people to know about depression. 'Listen to the radio program on Sunday,' he said.

I can remember being in the car, switching the program on and hearing him. I turned to Catherine and said: 'That's not Craig.' You could tell from the way he was talking that

203

he was too hyped up. He was too much the other way. You know when Craig is passionate about something, but he was way beyond that.

Did I communicate that sentiment to him? I can't remember, which makes me suspect now that I didn't. My response was that he was going through some tough times, and although I didn't really understand depression or how it occurs and how or whether you can recover from it, I felt reassured that he was getting professional help. Listening to him that day, he definitely sounded hyped up and I knew he was passionate about the subject. But we had become used to Craig being at the forefront of so many things. I guess what reassured me was that he actually knew what he had and wasn't hiding from the fact that he had depression. He wasn't bottling it up inside. From what I was hearing, many people don't talk about it and that becomes a huge problem in itself. At least Craig was communicating what he had been going through. He was being upfront about it by saying, 'Yes, I've got depression, I've sought help and I want to tell people. There is too much of this problem hidden in the closet.'

My take on it was that although it certainly didn't sound like Craig on the radio that day, at least he was admitting it and getting the right help. He knew he had to look after his lifestyle a bit better and have some form of relaxation. So, I took heart from that.

But then the Olympics were coming up. As a broadcaster he was very passionate about such a big undertaking. To have the opportunity to go to the Olympics in your own country and actually broadcast it is no small thing. So, it seemed like he was thinking that he had everything under control again and was throwing himself back into the work environment to see just how far he could go with the Games.

Different jobs bring their own pressures. You have to be mindful of that and try to strike a balance so that you have time to work, rest, relax and spend time with your family. My cricket career ended because I could no longer devote enough time to it to get the same enjoyment. Now, I play a bit of golf and competition squash. The balance works better and allows me time with Catherine and our three boys. As blokes, we all see ourselves as bulletproof and manage things in a way we believe works best for us. But Craig's problems did make me stop and think, yes, I do have a huge workload and I must make sure there is suffi-cient time for rest and family.

Both Craig and I enjoy a drink. When you throw those drinking nights on top of the workload you find you're burning the candle at both ends. In the business he is in, there would be plenty of opportunities for a big night out. Eventually, it all became too much.

———

Peter and I made that one visit to James Fletcher. The next time we saw him, he was at home. It was obvious he was much better. Whereas he had been very confused when we saw him at the hospital, we felt reassured that he knew what was going on. Understandably, the hospital environ-ment had been very strange and might have accounted for some of his confusion. Back home, he seemed much more settled and less bewildered by it all. Once he had been diagnosed and started to accept the reality of bipolar and the medication that went with it, you could sense his improvement. Again, he was upfront about it and determined to give himself the best chance of managing the condition. He wanted to talk about the positives, to look forward rather than back.

The question people might ask is whether the Craig Hamilton I know today is the same person I'd known before he was hospitalised. I don't look at it in that light at all. I view it as an illness which can be treated. If he has it under control we can still go out for a beer every now and then and life can go on more or less as normal.

Some people can joke about such setbacks but we don't. Could I joke about it if he had another form of illness? Well, put it this way: if whatever was wrong with him was as serious as this has been, I certainly wouldn't be joking about it. From where I'm standing I can see that it impacted on him greatly. I don't go into how much strain it placed on his relationship with Louise but can assume it must have been very difficult for both of them. As a mate I want him to know that I'll always be there when he needs to speak to someone. In the meantime, I just hope he is going okay.

If there is a message in it for the rest of us it's about the value of balance in our lives. It's also important to keep in touch with your mates, asking how they're going and being upfront with each other about how we really feel at the time. I know that's hard for most of us – it's been bred into us to simply answer, 'I'm fine.' But if you wait until you see obvious signs that someone you care about is really struggling, it may be too late. Most of us wouldn't know how hard it is to recognise the symptoms of depression let alone admit that it might be happening to us.

I don't think it has changed him as a person but rather encouraged him to make adjustments. Basically, he's still the same old Craig – an excitable kid in a grown-up's body. He still enjoys a beer and a laugh. For a long time he must have been wondering what was happening to him. I think it was that competitive part of his nature that made him take a long time to admit he was suffering from something that was quite serious. But once he was diagnosed and when he finally came to grips with that, he was well on the way to being able to manage it. Now, I believe his attitude is: 'I know I've got this problem and it is quite serious. But if I look after it in the right way, I'll still be able to live the life I want to live.'

Don't get me wrong – he's still got that competitive streak. When we play tennis he still wants to win. A few weeks back we went to Terrigal for a picnic. We took the kids across the park for a game of cricket and he bounced me twice. It was that old competitive streak harking back to the days when we were rivals at Charlestown and Belmont. After he bounced me the second time I looked down the pitch and saw the same old Craig Hamilton. We both laughed.

16

'LOOKING FOR ANSWERS': SCOT LEIGHTON, BEST MATE

Craig came up here for a family barbecue and told us he was having a bad spell. On that day he walked into the kitchen here and had a yak with me and Matty, Louise's brother. I can't recollect the entire conversation, but he never actually said he had a depressive illness. Instead, he talked about being tired, flat, off his food and feeling pretty run down. The impression was that he didn't want to put a tag on it. As an indication of how bad he was, later that afternoon he was standing out the front thinking about going for a walk down to the other end of the golf course and back.

'What for?' I asked.

'Just for something to do.'

'Don't be an idiot. It's not going to help you. Just sit down and take it easy.'

That's how vague he was at the time. He thought that going for a walk of a kilometre or so in his condition might be a good idea.

I'd known for a while that this was coming on. A few times on his way home from the football of a Sunday evening he had phoned me up for a bit of a yak. In those calls he mentioned he was doing it tough getting to games, it was wearing him down and the excitement had gone. He couldn't understand what had happened to his energy levels. My wife Christine is not only Louise's sister but her best friend. They talk nearly every other day and we were getting the idea that something wasn't quite right. But nobody could put their finger on a specific illness.

When Craig started telling me that he was feeling flat my response was, 'Ease up. You've got to learn to just sit down and relax. When you get home you don't need to go for a run down the beach or anywhere else. You've got to learn to just take it easy. Watch TV, have a beer with your mates. Take time to wind down.' He was giving himself no time to relax and simply unwind. Come to think of it, he was always on the go. Whenever we went out or had a holiday together, he would be looking for something extra to do. Everybody else would be taking it easy, but not Craig. I didn't mind because he'd keep the kids amused with a game of cricket or rugby while I'd sit back with a beer and watch the test match on TV.

I've known Craig since about 1971 when we met up in

third grade. We became good mates. The attraction was sport – cricket and football in particular – and a similar sense of humour. We enjoyed taking the piss. Nothing was sacred. It's not like you could ever say the wrong thing. Everything was up for a crack. I find it easier to get on with people who are like that – you never run the risk of treading on their toes. Considering what's happened to him, it's good to still take the piss – after all, it's not as if I never had my problems.

Everything that he wanted to do, he would *smother* you in it. If he had cricket on his mind and wanted to bowl to someone, he'd be at you and at you to go for a practice. Kids usually take it in turn to bat and bowl, but he'd say: 'I won't bat, I'll just bowl, so long as you come and practise.' I'd tell him to get stuffed. Whenever there was a big match coming up it would be all-engrossing – a hundred percent full-on. Tunnel vision.

I used to spend a lot of time down at his place. Dick, his dad, was a character – a very affable guy with social habits much like Craig's. He liked a beer more than Craig did and would go down the pub for a bit of a yak. Dick was enthusiastic, just like his son. Their style of speech had the same jauntiness. Like Craig, Dick was always pretty opinionated. They both enjoyed performing. Loved to get hold of the microphone. At Craig's fortieth birthday he got up and entertained us all. Luckily for Craig, nothing seems to embarrass him. Look at his breakdown: if that had happened to me you wouldn't have got me out of the house, especially if I had a bit of a profile like Craig. His breakdown occurred in a very public place – Broadmeadow railway station – but that aspect of it has never seemed to concern him.

Just before the Olympics he had phoned to say that he was going on the air to talk about depression and that we should all listen. It was painful, bloody painful. He was talking over the top of people. Talking at them and not listening. He was at the top of his voice, blaring flat-out and talking waffle. I hope there was more than one micro-phone in the studio because I had visions of Craig trying to wrestle it off the other two people. I don't think the third person in the studio got much of a word in. Craig had a message for everyone: 'People have to talk.' That was about the whole strength of what he had to say for an hour. 'I've got the tools now,' he was saying, 'and the message I have for you is that people have got to talk.' It was cringe factor thirty-plus. But I was soon beyond feeling bad about it because two days later he went off at Broadmeadow. As bad as that radio session sounded, we thought it was all part of his healing process, that it was something he just had to go through to get better.

We were all happy that he had sought help and, although the radio program was pretty awful, we viewed it as another part of his journey out of the woods. Yet there was something else going on. Even though he was out of the depression, he clearly wasn't himself. I was in regular touch with him during that time and he wasn't the Craig I'd always known. Instead, he was loud, talking at you, not listening. I phoned him on the Monday – the day after the radio show – to wish him all the best. He sounded like he was trying to do a few things at once, putting a salad sandwich into his mouth while talking at you and not hearing a word. And he was loud! I was on my mobile in the truck and a bloke standing outside could hear Craig. He was so loud with no inflections in his voice at all. He sounded like a drill sergeant-major. If I had thought to ask him about his health or state of mind, it would have been pointless because he wasn't listening.

My recollection is that Louise called Christine with the news that Craig had gone off the deep end at Broadmeadow and was in James Fletcher. We dropped everything and drove straight to the hospital. He was sedated and we didn't get to see him. Instead, my job was to bring the kids back to our place while Christine stayed with Louise. I saw Craig's brother Ian the next morning and told him as much as I knew. On the Thursday, I phoned the hospital from work and managed to speak to Craig, telling him I'd see him on the Saturday. I felt pretty uneasy about walking back into the psychiatric hospital. By then he was out of the high security wing and was waiting to meet me.

I don't know what I'd expected but he didn't seem worried by his predicament. He had a few bits of bark off here and there from his scuffle with the cops and looked a bit jaundiced from what I understood was a chemical reaction to his psychotic episode. Whether that's right or wrong, I'm not sure. Otherwise, he seemed pretty upbeat and not the least bit embarrassed about being in a mental hospital. That Saturday was the first day of competition at the Olympics but Craig was still talking about making it to

Sydney for the second week. We had a bit of a talk and he said, 'I'll run this past you,' as he rolled out his strategy for making it to Sydney for week two of the Games.

I looked at him and said: 'Athens.'

As usual, he wanted some activity so he and I played a game of bowls. Then I remembered I had left something in the car. He walked with me to the main gates which are left wide open. My car was parked about fifteen metres beyond the entrance. But when we came abreast of the gate, Craig stopped. This seemed strange at the time because we were in the middle of a conversation. I turned back as if to encourage him to follow me the extra short distance to the car but he said, 'No, I'll be okay. I'll just wait here.'

I tried to make a joke of it: 'I don't think there'll be too many alarms going off . . .'

'No, no,' he said. 'I'll just wait here.'

Back inside he gave me the rundown on some of his house-mates: the fella who thought his girlfriend was a pop star and the bloke with the card tricks always looking for someone to play a hand with him. It reminded me of being back in 1975 and watching *One Flew Over the Cuckoo's Nest*. I thought, there are some weird people in this place and if you're not worried about finding yourself in here with them, then there is definitely something wrong.

What troubled me was that he didn't seem to recognise that he had suffered a major trauma in his life and maybe it was time to sit down and reflect on what the hell had happened. Instead, he was just thinking about getting out of there and moving on.

Later, we heard that he had delusions about being Jesus Christ. I thought to myself, well, that may be as he understands it, but there are plenty of people who think that they've got The Message from somewhere or other.

For me, the crash on Broadmeadow station came as a bit of a shock. But, I was thirty-six, and by that stage you have seen a bit of life. My view was that before the crash he had sought professional help and, if qualified people hadn't been able to pick what was going on with him, then what chance a mental health virgin such as me?

As much of a shock as it was, it certainly gave me an insight into other people's problems. Just after that a bloke at work was going through a bad spell and they tried to sack him. The signs were there he was going through a process of instability and was tipping towards the edge. I was able to say to his workmates, 'Look, my brother-in-law has just gone through a mental breakdown and this bloke could be heading the same way. He needs our support; he doesn't need to be shunned.' It worked out all right. He got his job back after about six months.

After he was discharged from hospital, the biggest shock for Craig was how long it would take before he was allowed to work again. By then he had used up all his sick leave and that put a whole new series of stresses on the household. Somebody had to bring the money in and nobody knew just how, when or whether Craig would make it back to work. Given that he had already sought help once and had been considered okay to resume work and even go to the Olympics, the same mistake wasn't going to be made twice.

The doctor who finally gave him the green light would have to have been doubly sure that Craig was okay. Meanwhile, there was the frustration of wondering when or if he still had a career. That must have leeched out into the family as another form of stress. Life is never going to be normal when you are not working. You're wondering just what you can and can't afford and what sort of lifestyle adjustments you are going to have to make. It was tough for the family.

———

Craig is on a mission to shed some light on mental health through his own experiences. I don't know about that. Appearing on *60 Minutes* wasn't a good idea. It was treated in typical *60 Minutes* fashion – never getting down to the real nuts and bolts of the story. My reservation was that it didn't really approach the issue in a deep and honest fashion. On the other hand, at least it didn't degrade it, which was a relief. There is always somebody who will come out and say, 'Hey, I've had that and it's great to hear someone talk about it.' If that makes it all worthwhile, then well and good. Whenever Craig goes public on this somebody says, 'Good on ya, mate.' That may drive him on, who knows? He spoke about depression at a Chamber of Commerce lunch and he told me that two or three people came up to him to say that they had suffered from depression and were really glad he was doing something about it. *60 Minutes* did the same thing via viewers' letters which said the story had helped demystify the illness.

Most of us have a deep-seated prejudice about mental illness. After all, there is no reasoning with a crazy man. Human nature is a funny thing. You may get on very well with someone who is ill but when they turn on you, it leaves you wondering why you were so nice to them in the first place. It's like when the Kosovar refugees were staying at the Singleton Army Camp. One of them wanted to go home and kicked up a big stink about it by sitting on the bus all day and making his family join him. All those people who had done nothing for them but were quietly congratulating themselves for having the Kosovars here in our community suddenly turned on them and called for the lot to be sent back home. People can bring that same attitude to anyone suffering mental illness.

It's obvious Craig wants to tell this story and I couldn't stop him, even if I wanted to. I've known him so long that I don't get upset about whatever he wants to do. He is going to do it anyway. There are plenty of ways to make an arse of yourself and if he does it once or twice it's not going to worry him. He's a great public performer. That's his job and he knows how to avoid talking himself into a corner. So long as he's well and healthy. If it were me, I'd want to deal with it, get the help I needed, take the medication, manage it, but otherwise put the whole thing to rest. But there is no point wishing that on him. My sentiments would be pretty much the same as those of Louise: 'Why put yourself through the whole thing again?' You don't need having your kids picked on at school. But I don't think too many people are telling him that. Why? For two reasons: one – he is a very tough nut to debate against. The other is that it is a noble cause and he is a knight in shining armour. He loves telling this story because he wants to get the message across. Some people are just media junkies, aren't they?

He may have a profile but he's never been put on a pedestal within the family. If he was, I'd drag him down if he ever got too high and mighty. I enjoy taking the piss out of him as he does with me. To our kids he's just Uncle Craig. They seem to have handled the whole business of his breakdown pretty well because Christine did a good job explaining it to them. That day he was taken to hospital I was driving Josh, Amy and Laura back here when Laura said: 'The police had to come and get my daddy from the train station.' Very matter-of-fact. They were very quiet on the way home but otherwise seemed okay. Kids are funny – they tend to play every ball as it comes without looking at the wicket.

The irony in all this is that he used to say he had the best job in the world, enjoying the adrenalin rush of going to the football and getting paid for it. Meanwhile, I had to go to a shithole for my work. And yet, ultimately, I was happier with my lot than he was driving to and from the footy. There was obviously something very wrong there. Here he was with an adrenalin job and he was no longer getting a buzz out of it. Those calls he made to me on his way home from the footy telling me how flat he felt must have come at a time when he was feeling very lonely, looking for answers but not finding them. His body was telling him to keep going when he definitely needed to ease up.

My feeling is that he can now recognise the indicators and knows how to pull back before he gets too high and tips over the edge. Where does he go from here? I think he'd love to be calling the football and be the best in the business. But, it's a cut-throat game – only two networks broadcasting doesn't leave a lot of room to manoeuvre. If he switched ships he might find himself working for a more demanding employer.

I think Craig is still ambitious but he respects the ABC's values. It's a bit of a left-wing organisation which suits his politics. More importantly, it pushes quality as opposed to garbage. You have to consider that his current employer has been very sympathetic about Craig's condition. Not all employers are like that. From what I understand, there is no cure for bipolar disorder; instead, you have to manage it properly to live a fairly normal life.

I've told him that if he ever goes crazy in front of me, I won't be calling the cops. I'm going to hit him twice: once to knock him out to make the surrounding area safe – then, as he's going down, I'll hit him once for my own satisfaction.

17

'In Sickness and In Health': Louise Hamilton

When I first met Craig it was 'Whoa!' I'd never met anyone quite like him. He was such an extrovert, so full of life, everyone knew him and he was great to be around. We went places together, he was outgoing, played lots of cricket and he'd take the time to sit down and talk. We would go to parties or catch a band – he was never the type to sit around and do nothing. He was great fun without being an over-the-top show-off or the party animal that carries on like a dickhead.

It was a big deal for him to be in Newcastle while the rest of us were still at home living with the folks. Then I came down to Newcastle in 1983 to start nursing and lived in the nurses' home for two years. That was important because you got to know the other nurses. When you couldn't cope with the stress of the job it was great to have a chat in the tea-room with the others, hear about their experiences and how they dealt with life on the ward. It was very good for the head and the soul, especially when you're trying to get through that first difficult year of nursing.

Later, I moved into a place at Waratah with three other nurses. Craig and I got engaged in 1986 and rented a unit at Smith Street, Charlestown. Was there anything unusual about those times that could have been a clue for what lay ahead? He was working five days a week plus playing cricket while I was doing shiftwork. So, we might barely see each other for five days in a row. But when I started to do more regular hours and less shiftwork, a pattern started to emerge. He would go in blocks of partying hard, often to five o'clock in the morning. The binge. That block might last for a couple of weeks then he'd settle down, be fine for a while and then go again. He would tell you he was going to a party and you'd expect him home at two only to find him walking in at dawn. Hindsight tells me those blocks were actually periods of elevation. In those days I just put it down to him partying hard. Hey, everybody does that. But then it began to impact on me. I'd be working and worrying, losing sleep wondering when he was going to get home. When the kids came along, his partying affected me much more until it became an issue between us.

During his elevated phases he would exercise two or three times a day. He was playing first grade cricket but would exercise in addition to his normal training. It was not unusual for him to work all day, come home and go for a bike ride. Then he would head off to cricket practice after which he would come home and lift a few weights. The standard pattern in the early years was for him to exercise three or four times a week but then he started to add in the extra sessions. On top of that, he'd throw in a game of squash or tennis as well.

When the kids came along and we both had so many commitments, he would still make time to exercise. It was a selfish thing. He'd say, 'I'm going for a bike ride.' I'd tell him I didn't think that was fair but, in the zone he was in at the time, it was always your problem – not his. 'You've got a problem, I'm exercising, bad luck.' That's just the way it was. He'd party hard and bike-ride hard for a while and then he would settle down again.

In 1991 when Joshua came along, Craig had a down period and took time off work. He would probably call it depression. I wouldn't. He's a bit of a hypochondriac. When he's got a cold he calls it the flu. I would have called his condition 'physically worn out, mentally strained'. He was never medicated, never had to go and see anybody. Instead, he just took a big block of time off work, lazed around, stopped everything. At the end of eight weeks he was well again but had learnt nothing. He was straight back to his old routine of trying to conquer the world.

For the last six or seven years of working in the mine he didn't enjoy the job. It was hard yakka and difficult for him to turn up for work when he had his heart set on a different career. He loved the fellas and enjoyed the male company but it wasn't what he wanted to do for a job. Because his new life in the media was so attractive the other became less tolerable.

And then he took on the union job. It gave him a different avenue, meant he got out of the pit a bit more and created the chance for him to talk to people. It was an alternative to digging and shovelling coal. It was another level of responsibility, a sign that he never knew how to say 'no'. It wasn't until after 2000 that he learnt how to say 'no'. Until he fell off the wall, he didn't know how to say 'no' to anything. He simply took on more and more.

Where was I in all this? Any number of times I'd have something to say about him taking on another commitment, but he just thought I was whingeing. Craig couldn't see what impact him not being at home had on our household. It was a Catch-22 – he was never around to realise how hard it was for the rest of us. For a long period we would see him for two days a fortnight. We had two little kids, me working five or six days a fortnight, him working full-time as a coalminer and every weekend on the football. He would come home late on Sunday night and it was straight back on the hurdy-gurdy for another go. There seemed no end to it. It wasn't that he didn't love his kids – he adored them – but he was flat-chat on all these other projects. He was always on the go. Now that I think about it, even before that time, when we were on holidays he could never sit still. He would be off for a jog on the beach and as soon as that was over there would be something else to send him rushing off again. There never seemed a moment when we could just sit and relax. I'd say, *Just sit on the bloody beach and rest!'*

Now he can do that. Today, his holidays involve sitting down by a pool or beach and doing nothing. About the only real activity he gets involved in now is a game of touch footy or cricket on the beach with Josh and a nephew just before sunset. He's finally realised that you need downtime, that downtime is good for soul and good for self. It gives you time to rejuvenate. You can be busy without being over the top. But you still need time for relaxation and self. When you only get a couple of holidays a year, that's what you must do.

It got to a point where I realised something had to go. I can remember thinking, if this is what the rest of our life together is going to be like, I ain't having it.

When I'd catch him taking on too much I would buck and scream, but he would say: 'This is where I want to go. I have to put in the hours now to get payback down the track.'

It took me quite a few years to realise that he was actually going to make his dream career a reality. It wasn't a hobby. When Craig told me he had been offered a redundancy by the mine and asked me what I thought, twelve months before I would have told him to wake up to himself. But it had got to the point where I said: 'Why not?' We weren't seeing each other. We were earning plenty of money but we never went anywhere. It wasn't the way I wanted to live. I thought, hey, make or break, we've got to do something.

When we went to see Sandy MacNeil for financial

advice, I had a list of questions a mile long at the end of which I'd written, 'Are we crazy, or what?' So, I said, 'Sandy, are we crazy, or what?' and he said, 'No, go for it. You've got enough money. My only worry is you having twelve months off on maternity leave.' Our third child Laura was just four months old and I was still on leave. I said that I could give a month's notice and I'd be back at work earning again. So, we went for it.

Craig worked hard but he was home on a more regular basis. We had to watch the money at first. Before, we'd have takeaway when we felt like it or go out to a good restaurant and order up. Instead, we reverted to how we had been brought up. We went to the beach for entertainment and we'd take a packed lunch rather than buy takeaway. We had picnics, hired videos instead of going to the movies, held dinner parties instead of going to restaurants. We actually saved money. Any extra we earned was put away so that whenever Craig experienced a downturn in his work, we would have some savings to live off. It was good. Life had been the pits before the redundancy came along, but this was a terrific improvement for all of us.

The way I looked at it, the worst scenario would have been my going back to work full-time and Craig staying home to look after the kids. He couldn't have coped with that – he is too outgoing to be confined at home. And I wouldn't have coped with shiftwork and not being with the kids. So, we made a go of it, went back to basics, put our marriage back on track and concentrated on doing the simple things well.

The hardest part was going from hardly seeing Craig at all to having him home for almost twenty-four hours a day. I found out what retired women encounter when their husbands no longer go out to work each day. He'd be saying, 'What are we having for morning tea?' and I'd be thinking, well, I haven't made the beds or put a load of washing on yet! You don't realise the importance of routine or how organised your life has to be until somebody who has no idea of any of that intrudes on your day. Having Craig here butting into my domain totally threw me. There were things which had to be done. So, I came up with a ten-point plan and told him, 'We've got to do something here or I'm gonna kill you.' He had to start doing jobs like washing up, and adhering to a few rules for the running of the house. After all, quitting the mine meant that our home had become his base of operations and he was here all the time.

Despite all my misgivings he made a living – hosting trivia nights, writing newspaper columns, working for the radio, all sort of things – and I didn't have to go back to work until my maternity leave was up. The redundancy payout meant we owned our house and that made a world of difference.

Craig operated like that for a few years until he went full-time with the ABC in 1999. He applied for the job, had all the qualifications and I just assumed he would get it. I think I would have been more floored if he had come home and said that he been knocked back. It was great that he was working regular hours, going out the door each day and fitting into a routine. Once again we had regular money and life was easy. He was happy, enjoyed his work, but still took a lot on. But, from where I was standing, it was nowhere near as bad as it had been. People had no idea how hard it had been during the years he worked part-time. They would say to me, 'Isn't it great, he's got a full-time job with the ABC after only working there for twelve months.'

'No he hasn't,' I'd say. 'We've done ten years of hard slog to win this you-beaut position. Yeah, okay, he has Tuesday-Wednesdays off, goes to the footy on weekends, works nine to five plus Saturday mornings, the pay is good and so are the holidays. But, hey, we had ten years of shit to get here.'

How did I put up with it for ten years? Each time I got to a point where I was fed up, something would happen to make me refocus. Halfway through it, when Josh was four or so and Amy one or two, I can remember thinking, if this is it, I don't want any more to do with it. This is not what married life is supposed to be. That was about as far as my thinking would go. I never reached the stage of imagining myself as a single mum. Perhaps I felt like a single mum already. More importantly, you just get used to the routine. You start out and you take on more and more and it just becomes the norm. I didn't have time to dwell on it. I guess I wouldn't have known how to manage without the wage. Although he wasn't so much here in person, at least he was paying the bills.

And when he'd come home he would be wonderful with the kids. He'd play with them, entertain them, read to them and put them to bed. As little as it was, they would see the good bit of him. Joshua still idolises him. He thinks his dad is the most wonderful creature God ever put breath into. They all eventually work out that we're not perfect, that we all have our fallibilities; but at least you get a few years when they still believe in you. Of late, with Josh entering his teens, there are moments when they disagree and Josh won't speak to him for a while. There is already that sense of the bull and the young calf wanting to take him on. Actually, Craig said to him one day: 'This is my house and you can be king bull when you get your own house. But while ever you're here, you're just one of the calves, mate.'

Life was better but the partying continued. He still took on too much and he was still very self-orientated. I always called his elevated periods his 'selfish prick times'. That's when he would be '*me, me, me*'. He couldn't see outside of his world. In my time as a nurse I'd seen plenty of people in the middle of a family crisis. As an observer you can recognise things for what they are. But when it happens to you, when you're stuck in the middle, living it, you can only see the bits you can cope with. It all flies by and you can only take on so much. When he got sick in 2000 and said he was depressed, I said, 'No, we'll start with a few different things on the home front before we worry about your depression, boyo.'

In December-January, heading into the New Year, he was down and I suggested he should go and see a herbalist, try meditation, time management classes – do the alternative thing first. I put it down to taking too much on – being physically and mentally worn out. Being a nurse, I tend not to mollycoddle. I see enough seriously ill people in my daily work. When I'm sick, I just go into my room, get over it and come out when I'm well. No pussyfooting. Just do it.

Slowly but surely he was going down. He wasn't eating as well, he was grumpy and not his usual self. It was quite insidious. Then I'd find myself admitting: 'No, he's not real well.' He was talking about being down and not coping. I suggested it was time to go and visit the GP. Our doctor decided he was depressed and started him on tablets. Craig might be a hypochondriac, but he is not a pill-taker. He didn't want to go on the medication.

Looking back, he didn't tell me how low he was at the time. The antidepressant medication took about five weeks to kick in but he was plummeting fast. We were probably about two weeks too late. Had we started him on the medication two weeks earlier, he never would have sunk so far. In that phase he experienced a rapid decline. He was very depressed, hardly talking, not eating, spending most of his time in bed.

Shit, I've cried so much over this: one day, just as I was ready to go to work on afternoon shift, we had a conversation about a person who had taken his own life. I said, 'Craig, this fellow has committed suicide, what does that have to do with you?'

He didn't reply.

'You're not thinking about doing that, are you?'

And I looked at him and the thought hit me: *Bloody hell, you are!* It all sank in: you are a lot sicker than I thought. You have been hiding so many things. All I could think of was: *Holy shit! He is so sick. And I've got to go to work. I can't ring up at twenty-five past two and say I'm not coming in – they don't have the staff.* So, I left him with the babysitter. I thought, I can do this.

I've gone to work, crying the whole way. I don't even know how I got there. Walked in and one of the girls took one look at me and said, 'What's the matter?' and I said, 'My husband has just told me that he's suicidal.' She hugged me, worked out a way to get some staff there, put me in a car and took me to a girlfriend's place so that I could settle down enough before going home. I told my girlfriend what was going on and had a good cry. She's a nurse, she understood. She held my hand and listened. When I arrived home I just walked in the door and blasted him. I was so cranky, so angry. I called him the biggest arsehole God ever put breath into.

'How could you think of leaving us? What are you talking about? You've got to tell people . . . You can't hide these things . . . This is shit!' I was swearing and blasting him. At the same time I was thinking, Louise, you've got to be kind and understanding, but I was too angry. How could he think of leaving us and everything we had together? When I'd said my bit I sat down and cried again and thought, great, here we go. I rang work and requested time off.

I took a couple of weeks off to look after him, keep an eye on him and be certain that he wouldn't do anything silly. I stayed with him all the time. Craig wasn't in the mood to talk. He was really, really depressed. Just a shell. I think now that it might have been critical that I watched him so closely through that period. When I had challenged him about whether he was suicidal or not and he didn't answer, I thought: right, you are there. If I had to leave the house, he went with me. I wasn't letting him out of my sight.

I call it the 'mad cow' look. I've seen it so much in nursing. The patient looks very bland in expression, the face is often a bit flushed, the lights are on but nobody's home. They are not taking in the outside world. Their thought processes are too internalised. It's what you see on people who just aren't in the here and now. Craig definitely had it. After a few weeks of me being on tenterhooks watching him, his mood slowly began to rise. The medication started to kick in. During those weeks he hardly talked, ate little, took liquids and just slept. He lost kilos. It was hard work with three kids plus Craig to look after. He would be in the bedroom just lying there because he needed the rest, but I'd be thinking: *Just get up! Just come and help me to look after these kids for five minutes and give me a break.*

His condition continued to improve and by July–August I was confident enough to start saying to myself, 'We've made it!' But what did I know? At that stage I had no appreciation that antidepressants and bipolar were linked. My understanding now is that Craig has a predisposition to bipolar. He got depressed and they put him on an anti-depressant. The medication was one he should never use because he is bipolar. It takes too long to get into the system and too long to get out of the system. In other words the sufferer goes backwards, then he goes *bang* – elevated. And that's what happened to Craig. Give it to you or me and nothing happens, but bipolars who take it are vulnerable.

So, here we were cruising and me thinking that we had done it – we were out of the woods. The Olympics were approaching and he was as excited as all hell about going. The week before he was due to leave he started displaying bizarre behaviour. I took it as if he was a kid in a lolly shop so excited about going to the Games. I'm thinking, Craig, just *get* there. You just need to get rid of all this energy. You are so excited, so overwhelmed. The sooner you're in Sydney and stuck into the work the better. Not for one moment did I imagine it was the elevation component of bipolar. However, I was still thinking that he was weird, that his behaviour didn't make sense. Alarm bells were ringing. You know something is wrong but you can't quite put a name to it.

We were fighting a lot because he kept on telling me he wanted me to go to the Olympics but I couldn't get it through his head that I had too much on my plate to drag three kids down to Sydney. He sent me flowers at work for our anniversary – a day late after having forgotten it the day before. I hate flowers arriving for me at work. It was show-pony stuff – definitely not us. I was exhausted because he was sleeping for no more than three hours and was keeping me awake. He was ringing people all hours of the day and night, talking incessantly on the phone – friends, family, acquaintances – anyone he had taken a liking to. We had a $600 mobile phone bill for a period of two weeks.

He was going to bed really late, getting up early, going

for walks, exercising and skipping meals. I'd cook a meal for him and go to work only to come home and find the food still sitting in the microwave untouched. There I was throwing the food in the bin and thinking, this is really weird. I don't know what's going on. But that's as far as my thought processes went. I had work commitments plus three kids to look after and routine simply took over. I was too busy to allocate the time to sit down and think really hard about what the hell was going on with him. The only thing I could put it down to was that after ten years of him building up to his dream job, he was just so excited about going to the Games. He was like a kid in grand final week – I thought that the second he gets on the playing field he will use that energy in the right way and everything will make sense again.

When he said he was going on the radio to talk about depression I told him not to do it. I didn't think he was well enough. He insisted he was. My gut told me it wasn't a good idea. It was a Sunday morning and as coach he should have been at Josh's soccer presentation. Instead, I took Josh while Craig went into the studio. Before leaving he had phoned up every man and his dog telling them to tune in to the program. I didn't listen and I never will. On the way to the presentation I caught what turned out to be the last two sentences. It wasn't so much what he had to say but rather the strident way he was saying it, and I thought, *Oh, my God!* I tried to get hold of a mobile phone to ring the ABC to tell them to get him off. He was obviously sick and I was screaming inwardly, *Get him off, get him off, get him off!*

Recently, I was talking about that day with my sister Christine. 'I really should get hold of that program and listen to it,' I said.

Christine said one word: 'Don't.'

After Craig had his breakdown Madeleine Randall rang me. She thought it was her fault. I said to her: 'Madeleine, you couldn't have got him off that radio even if you'd wanted to. It was something he had to do.'

———

The train was due to leave at about four o'clock that Tuesday afternoon and he was running late, which is odd for Craig. Throughout that day he had been strange, but I had no idea he was delusional. At the station I was talking to Kathy Stewart, who I hadn't seen since Laura was born, and it was great to catch up. I was telling her that Craig had been through a rough spot but now he was going to the Olympics . . . *and this tremendous cackle came out of nowhere.* I'd heard that mad cackle before – at work – from people suffering mental illness. I turned around and looked *and it was coming from Craig!*

'Are you all right?' I asked.

'Yep, yep, just gotta get on this train. Gotta go.'

It's right what they say about fight or flight. I said to Kathy, 'I've gotta go,' and I just packed up the kids and made ready to leave. My guess is that nobody else on that platform recognised that cackle for what it was. Once you've heard it and know what it represents it sticks with you forever. With the kids back in the car we drove to

McDonald's at Broadmeadow and grabbed something from the drive-through. I walked back into the house as the phone was ringing. It was no more than ten minutes since I'd left the station.

Kathy said: 'Get down here. He's going off.'

'What do you mean?'

'Just get down here!'

I knew something was really wrong.

'I haven't got anybody to mind the kids.'

Kathy told me to bring them as her daughter, who is in her twenties, was at the kiosk and would keep an eye on them. We headed back to the station where, thank heaven, the kids were taken straight into the kiosk and distracted by free lollies and crisps. By then Chris Williams, Kathy's husband, had arrived and was standing on the platform.

Craig was sitting on a bench and I went up to him and said, 'What's the problem?'

'Thank God you're here,' he said. 'They told me you were dead.'

'Craig, I'm here. I'm not dead.'

He started swearing his head off, saying that was no good because it meant we were both dead.

'Look, it's all right,' I said, trying to calm him. But he was raving about Jesus Christ and the realisation hit me: *I get it – you're psychotic.*

I could feel the great sense of release escape from my body. This explained everything. 'Okay, I can deal with this. This isn't so bad.' Meanwhile, he was pacing, swearing, shouting, but he wasn't threatening.

They must have stopped the trains because Broad-meadow is a busy station and not a single one went through the whole time I was there, which might have been the better part of an hour.

After following and keeping an eye on him for a while I went back to the kiosk and phoned our GP to get the number for the Mental Crisis Team. He wasn't there but another doctor came on the line and I told him what was happening, that Craig had been depressed and now this had happened and I needed somebody to come and pick him up and take him to James Fletcher. He gave me the number. I rang the Mental Crisis Team and they told me to ring the cops. I approached a man who I took to be the station master. He said the police were already on their way.

At no time on the station platform did I think Craig might have been planning to kill himself. But later, when I sat down in the waiting room at James Fletcher, my mind went: *Holy shit! He was looking for a train to jump under?*

Since then, I've had a rethink: elevated people don't think about suicide. He was going to Sydney with a message. He had no reason to kill himself. He was going to conquer the world. Thank God he went psychotic before he could do the conquering. Back in May or June, when he had been depressed and suicidal, jumping under a train might have been an option. But he was no longer depressed, he was beyond elevated, he was psychotic. Craig had no idea what was going on. He was in a world of his own.

I arranged for a girlfriend to look after the kids while Kathy drove me to James Fletcher. Chris stayed to mind the kiosk. I told Kathy I'd be fine but she insisted, 'No, you're not going in there by yourself.'

At that point I wasn't thinking our lives had fallen down the toilet. I had been churned up and worried the week before. Once I saw the psychosis, I was relieved. My training told me that it is something from which you can recover. You get well. As for the bizarre behaviour leading up to that day – I had no name for it, no explanation. But as soon as I saw what was going on at the station I thought, *Okay, you've been elevated, now you're psychotic. I get it! This isn't so bad. We can fix this!*

———

'So, he does drugs –' I had to interrupt the young registrar at James Fletcher and tell him that my husband didn't do drugs. We talked about Craig's history and I think the registrar mentioned bipolar and the possibility of becoming elevated after having taken the antidepressants. At that stage I got a bit upset and mentioned that he might have been trying to jump under a train. The doctor told me that Craig would be in lock-up for a few days. It was early evening, the kids needed me and there was nothing more I could do at the hospital. I went home. The phone rang sometime between eleven and midnight and a nurse asked if I would accept Craig's call. From the ensuing conversation it was clear that he knew he was in hospital and that I was Louise.

'When I get out of here, I'll be going to the Olympics,' he said. No matter where I steered the conversation, he brought it back to the Olympics. Olympics, Olympics, Olympics.

'I'm freezing cold,' he said.

'Well, you hang up and I'll talk to the nurses and we'll get some blankets for you.'

The next day, I went to see him. He still had the mad cow eyes but was calm.

Craig spent ten days in hospital and we could see he was getting better. The mad cow eyes went after about four or five days. He was still a bit over the top wanting to play this game or throw himself into that activity. But he'd sleep all night.

No sooner did he show signs of improvement than he wanted to get back on the move and return to work. My view was that he had been unwell for twelve months and needed time to rest mind and body to give himself the best chance of making a full recovery.

It would take him a long time to admit that it was bipolar, that it is forever, that you need to go to psychiatrists and you need to take pills. Since then he has made major changes in his lifestyle: he doesn't drink, he does yoga, he knows how to say no, he takes time out, work is no longer the be-all and end-all of the universe. And, just as a side-line, he's found God. I say: 'It's funny that you've found God when you thought you were Him.' The joke in my family is: trust Craig to pick Jesus Christ – he couldn't have picked the Prime Minister, Gandhi or whoever – it had to be the top guy.

Talk about hard-won lessons. I believe things happen for

a reason. Craig needed to re-evaluate his life. Some people are tapped on the shoulder but miss the message. That's why Craig had to really hit the wall. Hindsight provides such a wonderful view. We could have taken him to a psychiatrist a week and a half before the Olympics and the doctor would have said, 'Look, he's elevated. It's bipolar, here are his pills.' But that didn't happen. I hammered myself for six months after the event saying, 'You're a bloody nurse – you should have picked it up.' But when you are in the middle of it you never get the overview. You are in the eye of the cyclone.

Eventually, the only realisation you can come to is: it was meant to be. Craig needed to reassess his life. What I was saying to him wasn't working. He needed to do something horrendous so that he could re-evaluate and really change his lifestyle. If we had caught him at the elevated stage he would have taken the medication for a few months and when he felt better simply got off them. But now, he doesn't want to ever go back to that place. He didn't enjoy it and neither did we. If the lesson hadn't been so powerful and hadn't made Craig reprocess his thinking, it would have been a much harder haul. It's Craig's nature to do everything hard, fast and big; but this time, he's had to learn a hard, fast and big lesson.

Why did I stay through it all? I never thought of leaving. Some days he gives me the bloody shits and I could punch him into next week. But I couldn't have walked away even if I'd wanted to. I'm not that type of person. I'm nothing brilliant, but I always thought we'd be together for the long haul. We've had great times together. I enjoy his company and the things we do as a couple and a family. He's still entertaining and good fun, he shows me things I'd never do off my own bat. On the other hand, I suppose I'm the constant – the one who is at home keeping the routines. I'm a coper, just plodding along, taking it all on and continuing to move along. That's life.

There was a time after the breakdown when he turned to me and said, 'That must have been awful looking after me through all that.' But, no, it wasn't like that at all. It was hard work but there wasn't enough time away from it to entertain the thought, hey, this isn't much fun! Instead, it was just a matter of getting in there and doing it, hoping that somewhere, someday, it would come out all right. And there was no reason why it wouldn't. Just because you have had depression and become psychotic, there is no reason to think that you can't get better. If you get the right help and you learn from the experience, there is every chance that you can recover well enough to lead a great life. I know that from personal experience. Eventually, we were going to get out of that rut.

Now is a good time in our lives. We have enough money not to stress about our finances. Our kids are well and healthy and so is Craig. Life is good. Don't think for a moment that we don't have our quarrels – we do. But most of the time our life together is great. I believe that so long as the good times outweigh the bad, you are on a roll.

Craig is not the only one who has learnt. We all have. Now, I can pick out a bipolar sufferer in a flash. There's a lot of it about. Before, when I encountered suicides and depression through work, I used to think, how could you have let it get that bad? Now, I have far better empathy. I'm in a position to tell them how much they need to have their friends and families close. They need somebody to remind them of the value of counselling. Having gone through it gives you a different perspective. It's like when somebody has a baby and you ask after the newborn. But, if you have kids of your own, you always ask about the mother first. When people used to ask after Craig when he was ill, sometimes I'd find myself thinking, just once, I'd like them to ask how I'm going. Nobody ever did. So, when somebody is ill I ask after them but always add, 'And how are *you* going?'

It's hard on the families. I'm here to say they shouldn't feel guilty about not liking the sufferer at certain times. That's okay. And it's all right to admit: 'This is a horrible place to be'. Sometimes you do feel like banging a head against a brick wall because the sufferer can frustrate you so much. The difference is you don't. Instead, you tell yourself that we will come out the other end.

The other day a man who I don't know very well at all approached me and told me his wife was suffering depression. 'How did you cope?' he asked.

'What do you mean?'

'Did you get frustrated?'

'Frustrated? Sometimes I wanted to smack his head into a brick wall!'

'Oh!' and he let out a great sigh of relief.

I laughed and said, 'It's okay, you're allowed to think it – just so long as you don't actually do it! No doubt your wife will want to come off the pills in a few weeks because she is feeling so damn well, and you'll want to give her another slap. Instead, you just talk to them, tell them how frustrated you are and then you go for a long walk.'

All through this I kept a watchful eye on the kids, wondering how or if it would affect them. If we could only look at the world through the eyes of a child. After the incident on the station Amy and Laura knew Craig was in hospital and I told them Dad was sick in the head.

'So, will he have a bandage on his head?' Amy asked.

'No. You know when people get sick in the heart and you can't see it?'

'Yes.'

'Well, that's Dad, except he is sick in the head, not the heart.'

Joshua wanted to see him. He kept asking questions, pacing around, quite unsettled by it all. He's a bit intuitive. Three days after Craig landed in hospital, I took the kids in for a visit. The girls took one look at him, noted he was pretty much how they last saw him and were fine with that. Joshua stayed close, sat on the arm of his chair, patted him, followed him around, touched him and remained very attentive. Josh was happy to be with his dad, but he knew he was sick.

The other day, somebody tried to commit suicide at Joshua's school. A young bloke tied a rope around his throat and jumped off the bridge into the canal. Quite a few kids saw it. Josh came home and said: 'You'll never guess what happened at school today. This fella – not one of the school kids – came into the ground and jumped off the bridge. It didn't work – the rope broke. He's got a cut under here, he hurt his arm and hurt his head.'

'Well, Joshua,' I said, 'that means he's really depressed. When people get really depressed and sick in the head they don't think life's worth living and they try to kill themselves.'

'Yeah, that's what this bloke tried to do. I just don't get it. Why didn't he go to James Fletcher – they fix you there.'

'Maybe this guy didn't know James Fletcher was open to help people like him. Josh, if you ever get that sad where you don't think life is worth living, come and talk to us, or talk to a friend, or go to James Fletcher or a doctor.'

And, as Josh toddled off, I turned to Craig: 'If nothing else, the kids will have the life skills to, hopefully, know what to do if anything like that ever happens to them.'

———

The man I'm looking at today is not the same person I met all those years ago. He's not as self-centred. Now, that sounds awful because you might think I'd been living with a horrible man, which wasn't the case. It was simply that he wasn't very tolerant. Back then, we did things his way. If he said we were going out, you went out. It wasn't worth rocking the boat not to go. We spent our time perpetually on the go because Craig was on the go. Now, we don't do that anymore. We don't ride the hurdy-gurdy. Instead, we have plenty of time sitting around doing nothing.

Craig is much more tolerant in every way. He is much more understanding of people's frailties. His insight into others is so much better. Now, he has empathy. Before, he didn't. Today, he's softer around the edges. He's not the same bloke I married but I still love him as much as the day we were wed. He's my soul-mate.

EPILOGUE

INSPIRATION

Self-trust is the essence of heroism.
Ralph Waldo Emerson

It's a long journey back from a mental breakdown but my trail is lit at intervals by the positive feedback from people who have managed to reach out for help. That affirmation is so important to me because not a week goes by when I don't hear a personal account of an individual or family caught in the anguish of mental disorder. Making a cause of mental health awareness is no light load. At times when I feel overwhelmed by the sheer volume of sufferers compared with the wasteland of public ignorance about the subject, I feel momentarily demoralised and ponder my choices. Why have I taken on this cause? Instead, should I have concentrated solely on getting well and putting this entire issue behind me? As a person who suffered a mental breakdown and still may be very vulnerable to further setbacks, am I even qualified to be an advocate for this cause?

But, just when this cycle of negativity begins to swirl, I have disciplined myself to hit a switch – one guaranteed to halt pessimism in its tracks. The switch is marked Inspiration and is powered by the example of two amazing characters. When I was younger I believed that heroes were famous, larger-than-life individuals who strode our national sporting arenas, people with the drive and willpower to reach extraordinary heights. Now, I realise that you can find heroes in any neighbourhood, on any street. Let me tell you about two I know who remain constant motivators, especially whenever my spirits run low or I start to doubt myself.

Steven and Clive Andrews were twins born on 1 January 1963. We went to the same schools, played football and cricket together and Steven married one of Louise's close friends. He was a go get 'em sort of guy who never took a backward step. Playing football, he was totally fearless, perhaps too tough for his own good. He broke his jaw in two places and had blood pouring out of his mouth yet refused to leave the field. Steve had a pain tolerance level that the rest of us couldn't even comprehend. Like most of his mates, he took a job in the mines and from there graduated to the Mines Rescue Service.

In the early nineties he was performing a training drill involving an abseiling exercise on a flying fox at one of the Upper Hunter's big open-cut mines. He was 30 metres up in the air when a cable gave way and dropped him the full distance to solid earth with nothing to break his fall except his arms and legs which he had extended in a desperate attempt to cushion the impact. He should have died. In fact, his heart stopped at the site but they were able to revive him. He incurred compound fractures of both arms and legs, serious spinal fractures and awful internal injuries.

They brought him from Singleton down to Newcastle and two days after the accident I dropped in to see him at John Hunter Hospital. It was a shocking sight: after surgery, they had put him back together like Meccano Man with steel rods protruding from both arms and legs. You've never seen a more likely candidate for a life spent in a wheelchair. When they could do no more for him they sent him home, where perpetual pain was his closest companion. The story goes that he returned to surgery in the hope of alleviating the pain from his broken back but when they opened him up and looked at the damage to the spinal column one surgeon reportedly asked: 'So, why are we doing this procedure?'

'To alleviate his back pain,' answered his fellow.

'But he's a paraplegic, isn't he?' queried the first.

'No, he's still walking.'

The first surgeon returned his gaze to the damage and shook his head in disbelief.

The accident should have killed Steve but instead it threw his life upside down. The family had to move to Queensland because the cooler winters of the Upper Hunter were more than his broken bones and ruptured joints could stand. When the family drives south for a return visit he can't sit up in a car. He's a 41-year-old man in a 71-year-old's body. Does this guy view himself as a victim? No, not for one second. Does he mention his accident? Never. Does he wallow in self-pity? Nope. Does he have a constant smile on his face? Nine times out of ten. There's no doubt he goes about his life experiencing far more pain than anyone could ever imagine but his outward demeanour is one of acceptance and grace. Steve Andrews doesn't live in the past; he exists in the moment and makes the most of it. He's an inspiration to his family and everyone who knows his story.

Steve Christie first came across my line of sight as a supremely athletic opening bowler for Waratah-Mayfield, sending bullets whistling past the ears of my Belmont teammates. We became great rivals and even better friends. He was charismatic, easy-going and as strong as a bull. It came as no surprise to me to learn that he was as proficient at rugby as he was at cricket – muscular, competitive, but with a heart of gold. We were picked in the same Newcastle and New South Wales Country representative cricket teams and shared countless laughs. One weekend in Sydney we ran into the New South Wales opener Scott Hookey, who was enjoying a big night out. When the introductions were completed and Scott had deduced that Steve and I were opposition bowlers, he slurred good-naturedly: 'I'm gonna cart you blokes tomorrow.' We looked at each other and said: 'Yeah, right.'

The next day Scott scored 186 during the course of which he smacked both Steve and me out onto the highway outside Bankstown Oval. I remember catching Steve's eye and both of us were laughing because we knew what the other was thinking: 'I hope the captain doesn't throw me the ball to bowl the next over.'

I was having a quiet beer at The Junction Tavern with cricket mates when somebody delivered the dreadful bulletin: Steve Christie was in intensive care and they didn't expect him to live. This couldn't be true – only a week earlier the local cricket community had celebrated when Steve had scored the winning runs for Newcastle in the final of the Country Cup. The grim news was confirmed – he had suffered an awful industrial accident which had exposed him to 33 000 volts, thrown him like a rag doll and should have killed him. The thought went through my mind that death might have been a mercy. He had suffered horrific burns to his arms, legs, torso and face. One ear was completely gone. For days his life hung by a thread.

Finally, he was out of intensive care and we witnessed his characteristic stoicism, the same gritty, fighting spirit leading him out of the darkest part of the trauma. First, he had won the fight to live. But then he faced the much, much longer battle to restore his life – eternal skin-graft operations, countless hours of painstaking burns therapy and physio. As his wounds slowly healed he wore a body stocking to reduce the dreadful scarring effects. Months after Steve's release from hospital, I was still shocked by the sight of him. He was a mess.

Like Steve Andrews, he was married with a couple of kids and the issues they must have faced as husbands and fathers would have been similar. But, once I spoke with Steve Christie, it was apparent that whatever force had destroyed his health and almost taken his life hadn't snuffed out his indomitable spirit. A week before the accident he had been at the height of his powers, the match-winning hero and the very essence of vitality. In a second, a terrible quirk of fate had taken all that away from him. Yet, there was no way he saw himself as a victim despite the demons he had to face and the constant reminders of how wonderful his life had been before the accident.

Waratah-Mayfield and the Newcastle district cricket premiership moved on without Steve Christie. But a few seasons later, word came out of Waratah that he was back running. Who would have thought it possible? Then came more news: he was back playing fourth grade cricket. Impossible! The scar tissue on his bowling arm was so terrible that it had virtually locked up his limb. Somehow, he had broken through that physical barrier to free his arm enough to bowl again. The bulletins continued: he was starting to work on his fitness and strength and had been promoted to third grade. Steve's mates around the cricket traps simply shook their heads in wonder when they heard the news that he was starting to rediscover a bit of pace and was sorting out a few of the third grade batsmen. How could he do this? It defied physical law.

You know where this story is heading. That's right, *Steve Christie made it back to first grade cricket*. He couldn't bowl the lengthy spells he once did – the accident had taken too much out of him. But when he sent them down in five-over bursts, it was a glimpse of the old champion stirring up the premiership's best batsmen. Now, if you think this yarn has finally run out of miracles, there's one more. He made it back to play rugby once again. Not for one moment did he dwell on his accident, nor did he ever look back and say: 'Poor bugger, me.'

Like the Steve Andrews story, a moment's thought about what happened to Steve Christie and how he dealt with it inspires me beyond belief. Shit happens and it certainly dropped a big load on those two blokes. But what happened *next*? They refused to be victims. They made a choice.

My trauma seems small compared to their experiences. Life will always throw tests at us – both large and small. How we respond to those tests is the key to our happiness. Whenever I find myself losing sight of that simple wisdom my thoughts turn to the two Steves. They remind me that we can command miracles, simply with the power of choice. That power resides in all of us but sometimes we have to suffer before we identify the true scope and purpose of that power.

Perhaps life's experiences are really a succession of concentric circles leading us towards a central point of wisdom. Sometimes we miss the cues and get lost. Other times we stumble upon a truth and it points us further down the road. I can't help but think that this process was keeping watch over me throughout my experiences. In Fletcher Park, Newcastle, near the hospital which bears his name, stands a pretty impressive cue or reminder – a statue of James Fletcher. His fame is virtually limited to the Hunter, which is a pity because he is one of our nation's greatest pioneers and nation-builders. Publisher, politician, civic leader and visionary, James Fletcher was also founding President of the Hunter River Miners Mutual Protective Association.

One hundred and fifty years ago (to the month in which I am writing this passage), miners at the AA Company's mine founded the association. It came after a three-week strike from which the miners won a pay rise and a company-subsidised sick and accident fund. It was the first in Australia and the forerunner for workers' compensation and occupational sick pay benefits. Fletcher wasn't a saint in the conventional sense, but in a way his wisdom and foresight have taken care of me, firstly as a miner and more recently as a patient at the hospital and beneficiary of the funded sick leave that underpinned my recuperation. The care he bestowed upon his community has left a great legacy, and it's an example I intend to heed. The least I can do with my experience is to use it to benefit others.

As I apply the finishing touches to this book, it occurs to me that there will be a certain resonance about the timing. Once again, four years after those events of 2000, we are in an Olympic year. Is there a painful echo here to call me back to the anguish of my breakdown? No. I was never listed to go to Athens and I've barely given it a moment's thought. Yet, subconsciously, reminders will emerge of the fact that I suffered a breakdown and ended up in hospital. That's fine – what's important is how I *choose* to react to those reminders. Life, as the Dalai Lama will tell you, is about impermanence. Every action creates a reaction and the choices we make shape our world. There is no way I'll be making negative choices. While the images of the XXVIII Olympiad are bouncing off satellites, I'll be engaged in the final rounds of another football season, creatively and joyfully occupied. Why? Because that's the choice I have made.

There are no regrets, only gratitude – gratitude that my crash came in time for me to learn vital, life-saving lessons. I now know that if you haven't got your health, family and happiness, you've got nothing. My miracle is that I flew close enough to the sun to lose all three. Instead, I survived and came out the other side with all the essentials intact and a new appreciation of health and happiness. As a progress score, it's looking pretty good.

TESTIMONIAL

Craig Hamilton's story is one of pure courage and iron will to break through the bonds of darkness that mental illness can bring. By inner reflection he was able to overcome his worst fears and in doing so has become one of the most inspirational people I have ever met.

I have known Craig Hamilton for seventeen years and for the past ten years I have seen him rise to prominence as a radio and newspaper personality. He is a very distinctive figure in rugby league circles and is renowned for his professionalism and enthusiasm.

In my mind Craig Hamilton's achievement in overcoming the horrendous effects of mental illness far outshines his professional success. I witnessed with my own eyes the challenge he and his family faced.

There are so many people suffering from mental illness and it is uplifting to see that it can be beaten. Craig's is a fascinating story, one that will endear itself to everyone in our community.

Paul Harragon
Newcastle Knights Premiership winning Captain

ACKNOWLEDGEMENTS

Writing a book is an incredible privilege and brings big responsibilities. We gratefully acknowledge the assistance of the Hamilton and Kelly families and particularly the love of Maureen, Dick and Ian Hamilton and Kate Hamilton Bennett.

We offer thanks to the management and colleagues at ABC Radio, staff at James Fletcher Hospital and the many individuals whose loving care has helped us make this incredible story into a book. These include Cath Kirkman, from NBN Television Jim Callinan and Melinda Smith, Stephen Crowe, Paul 'The Chief' Harragon and Andrew 'Joey' Johns at the Newcastle Knights, friends Siobhan Jackson, Scot Leighton, Peter Dunn, Wayne Fowler, Peter Schacht, Grant Rodgers, Barry Smith, Tom Hoppe, Chris

Williams and Kathy Stewart, and Dr Alan Weiss and Dr Tony Saltis. Thank you to Wayne Bennett for his support and for writing the magnificent foreword.

At Random House we would like to thank publisher Jane Southward for backing the idea for many months before the first manuscript arrived, editors Jo Jarrah and Zoe Walton for their attention to detail and marketer Elissa Baillie and publicist Benython Oldfield for helping us get the message out.

Depression is a common illness yet too often people hide the truth of their own or their loved one's condition. We wrote this book in the hope that Craig's story of recovery would encourage others – sufferers or their families – to seek help.

Craig Hamilton
Neil Jameson
July 2004

CREDITS

Acknowledgements are due to the following people or organisations for permission to include photographs:

Common Cause Magazine (finishing a shift underground)
Stefan Moore (Craig interviewing Paul Harragon)
Dragica Barac (Craig interviewing Allan Langer)
Simone Thurtell (half-time break at the State of Origin)
Ruth Hartmann (Craig with Dennis Lillee)
Maynard (Craig with Pat Rafter)

For more information about mental illness, go to:
www.sane.org
or call the SANE Helpline on Freecall 1800 688 382

For more information on the author, go to:
www.craig-hamilton.com